Tao Calligraphy to Heal and Rejuvenate Your Back

Tao Calligraphy to Heal and Rejuvenate Your Back

Dr. & Master Zhi Gang Sha
#1 NEW YORK TIMES BESTSELLING AUTHOR

Praise for Dr. and Master Sha

"The universe is not made of matter; it is made of information. Information that is aligned with the structure of the universe heals. The Dao Calligraphy of Master Sha is evidently aligned with the structure of the universe—it heals. Dr. and Master Sha is a true messenger of Dao."
— Dr. Ervin Laszlo
Founder of the Club of Budapest and
the Laszlo Institute of New Paradigm Research

"We, the human race, need more Zhi Gang Sha."
— Dr. Maya Angelou
author of *I Know Why the Caged Bird Sings*

"Practical, useful information and techniques for putting the body's natural abilities to work on healing —a wonderful contribution."
— Dr. Wayne Dyer
author of *Wishes Fulfilled: Mastering the Art of Manifesting*

"Dr. Sha is an important teacher and a wonderful healer with a valuable message about the power of the soul to influence and transform all life."
— Dr. Masaru Emoto
author of *The Hidden Messages in Water*

"Dr. Sha offers a clear, practical path to learning the secrets of self-healing."
— Marianne Williamson
author of *A Return to Love: Reflections on the Principles of A Course on Miracles*

"Dr. Sha's techniques awaken the healing power already present in all of us, empowering us to put our overall well-being in our own hands. His explanation of energy and message, and how they link consciousness, mind, body, and spirit, forms a dynamic information network in language that is easy to understand and, more important, to apply."
— Michael Bernard Beckwith
Founder of the Agape International Spiritual Center

"Dr. Sha makes available secret techniques and insights that were available in the past only to a select few. He shares in simple terms the insights and tools that took him more than thirty years of hard work and discipline to attain. He gives you access to information that wouldotherwise be unattainable."
— Dr. John Gray
author of *Men Are from Mars, Women Are from Venus*

"Master Sha is the most important healer and teacher available in North America today. Master healers are rare. Here is one of the living masters of soul healing and its effects upon mind and body."
— Dr. C. Norman Shealy
author of *Life Beyond 100*

"Master Sha's unconditional love for humanity will open your heart and touch your soul. He is one of the most extraordinary and powerful human beings I have ever met."
— Barbara DeAngelis
author of *Soul Shifts: Transformative Wisdom for Creating a Life of Authentic Awakening, Emotional Freedom and Practical Spirituality*

"Master Sha is divinely blessed and guided to heal the world and everything that is in it. From the smallest situation to the largest, he has the faithful gift of power to make things right."
— Roberta Flack
Grammy Award-winning musician

Heaven's Library Publication Corp.
30 Wertheim Court, Unit 27D
Richmond Hill, ON L4B 1B9 Canada
www.heavenslibrary.com
heavenslibrary@drsha.com

Waterside Productions
2055 Oxford Ave.
Cardiff, CA 92007
www.waterside.com

ISBN: 978-1-956503-96-8 print-on-demand
ISBN: 978-1-956503-99-9 print
ISBN: 978-1-956503-97-5 e-book

Design: Lynda Chaplin
Illustrations and cover: Henderson Ong
Animations: Hardeep Kharbanda, Yanan Wu

Contents

List of Figures

The Importance of Practice

THIS FIRST BOOK in my Tao Calligraphy book series includes soul-healing wisdom, knowledge, and practices for healing and transforming your health, relationships, finances, and more, with a focus in chapter ten on back pain.

The primary practice tool is Tao Calligraphy. Tao Calligraphy is Tao Source Oneness writing. It is art beyond art that can heal and transform your health, relationships, finances, spiritual journey, and every aspect of life.

Using two Tao Calligraphies that are included in this book, I will teach you how to practice in the Tao Calligraphy Field to transform not only back pain, but any aspect of life. The practices are simple but profound. Practice is essential for healing and transformation of any aspect of life. Practice is vital for you to receive the greatest possible benefits that I wish you and every reader to receive.

Practice. Practice. Practice.
Heal. Heal. Heal.
Transform. Transform. Transform.

Access the practice videos

Use the URL below or scan the QR code with your smartphone or other appropriate device to access the videos. A special app is not required.

https://tchryb.heavenslibrary.com

How to scan a QR code with your Android device

1. Launch the camera on your device.
2. Point it at the QR code.
3. Follow the instructions that appear on your screen.

How to scan a QR code with your iOS device

1. Launch the camera on your device.
2. Hold your device so that the QR code appears in the camera's viewfinder. Your device recognizes the QR code and shows a notification.
3. Tap the notification to open the link associated with the QR code.

Foreword

M Y WIFE GAYLE and I have worked intimately with Dr. and Master Sha for a decade. I have personally agented several of his most important books, starting in 2013 with *Soul Healing Miracles*, which was an Amazon number one bestseller. To date, Master Sha has had eleven *New York Times* bestsellers, of which four reached number one.

In 2014, I wrote *Miracle Soul Healer: Exploring a Mystery*, a biography of Master Sha in which I investigated his healing practices and was able to confirm hundreds of "medical miracles." Dr. Peter Hudoba, a former neuroscientist, has globally led nineteen clinical studies of more than six hundred subjects applying Dr. and Master Sha's methods and practices. All research results in relevant studies showed significant improvements in wellbeing.

I have a graduate degree in medical anthropology from Harvard University. One of my early scientific studies was published in the magazine *Yale Scientific* when I was a Yale undergraduate. I can confirm that the healings attributed to Master Sha and his trained healers far exceed any statistical correlation that could be attributed to the placebo effect. Although the precise mechanism for Master Sha's amazing results may defy current scientific explanation, new findings in quantum physics and other fields which are creating the new paradigm of "post materialist science" may offer insights into the understanding of what until now has remained a scientific mystery and anomaly.

Master Sha maintains that the mystery of his healing abilities can be understood by an analysis of Tao. This book explains in depth the nature of Tao. Tao is Source. Every element of life is contained within the Tao. You will learn how this works in this wonderful book.

When Master Sha first contacted me to be his literary agent, he did so because of my success with well-known spiritual authors and visionaries such as Eckhart Tolle, Neale Donald Walsch, Barbara Marx Hubbard, Barbara DeAngelis, Deepak Chopra, and many others. When we first spoke, Master Sha was most impressed by the success my company, Waterside Productions, Inc., had had in creating the For Dummies book series now published by John Wiley. As his publisher for ten years, my goal is for Master Sha to create a book series as popular and simple as the For Dummies series or the Chicken Soup for the Soul book series created by my friends Jack Canfield and Mark Victor Hansen. Both of these series have sold in excess of five hundred million copies. Gayle and I both believe Master Sha's Tao Calligraphy book series can reach this level of popularity. Although this and future titles in the Tao Calligraphy series require a greater commitment from readers to fully understand the principles presented than either of those two phenomenal book series mentioned, they are on another level even more accessible and should be even more popular.

Gayle and I believe this for several reasons. First, and most amazing, readers can benefit from these books without even reading them. Each book will include one or more Tao Calligraphies, unique works of art that carry a Source quantum vibrational field designed to transform specific ailments or improve specific life situations. This first volume you are reading addresses healing the back. If you have back pain, just hold the Tao Calligraphy image on the back cover against your back! You could receive relief and, for some, even recovery. You may or may not believe this is possible but try it. Not everyone will have an immediate positive reaction but many will. Master Sha never promises any result of any kind with any of his healing techniques and he always encourages everyone to consult healthcare professionals and continue with traditional medical regimens. This book is not a substitute for medical treatment. It is however a supplemental approach that has helped hundreds of thousands with no negative side effects. Five years ago, Gayle's daughter was diagnosed with fourth stage breast cancer and was gifted a healing calligraphy by Master Sha. The medical team was astonished when she showed no signs of cancer just a few months later. Her primary treatment modality was tracing the calligraphy and listening to Master Sha's Tao Song audio recording. Both Gayle and I were in disbelief but extremely grateful. Her daughter remains cancer-free to this day.

As Master Sha quotes from ancient Chinese wisdom: "If you want to know if a pear is sweet, taste it." Gayle and I strongly encourage you to taste this book. If you do have a positive experience, either immediately or over time as you continue to do the practices and study the wisdom, we would be delighted to hear from you. Please email your comments to TaoCalligraphyField@DrSha.com.

For those of you who want to truly understand the essence of Tao healing and why Tao Calligraphy has become such an effective healing modality, this is the best possible book for you to read. Gayle suggests that the first time you read this book, you skip the Chinese characters and focus on the practical exercises and summary conclusions provided in each chapter. For those wanting to go deeper, read the book a second time and focus on the Chinese characters and how they have been translated to English. Those who do this second reading will be greatly rewarded. Chinese calligraphy is a tradition that dates back thousands of years. The Chinese systems of Tao and energy healing date back to even earlier millennia. The wisdom Dr. and Master Sha has gathered from his studies and practices over the last six decades is unique. No other teacher or visionary on planet Earth at this time has developed such a clear explanation of why you can heal yourself once you learn to access Tao, the ultimate source of all creation. No other teacher gives you such simple and practical yet powerful tools and techniques for self-healing and self-transformation.

Master Sha's mission is to teach each of us that we can heal ourselves, we can heal others, and together we can heal our precious planet Earth. Use this book and share it with your circle of family and friends. In doing so, you will be contributing to your own wellbeing and that of our global community.

With best wishes for you to experience joy and accomplishment in every aspect of life.

William Gladstone with Gayle Gladstone, publishers of Waterside books, audios, non-fungible tokens, and online courses

Introduction

THE PURPOSE OF LIFE is to serve. I have committed my life to this purpose. To serve is to make others happier and healthier. To serve is to empower and enlighten others.

Millions of people have health challenges. A human being has four bodies: physical, emotional, mental, and spiritual. Human beings have countless health challenges in all four bodies.

Millions of people have relationship challenges with partners, children, parents, friends, colleagues, communities, companies, cities, countries, belief systems, and more.

Millions of people have financial or business challenges that can involve unemployment, debt, childcare, commuting, employee relationships, company structure and plans, financial controls, marketing, competitors, customers, suppliers, efficiency, effectiveness, and more.

Throughout the world, millions of people have major challenges in every aspect of life—with the environment, COVID-19, the economy, politics, fear, depression, anxiety, and more.

Millions of people are studying and searching for transformation toward solutions to all kinds of current challenges and conditions.

Why are Mother Earth and humanity suffering now?

Is there any way to transform all of these challenges?

If so, what is the way and how can we use it to transform the challenges?

This book will answer these questions and more. Most important, this book will offer practical techniques to transform the challenges.

In ancient Chinese wisdom, there is a renowned sacred teaching: da Dao zhi jian 大道至简. This means *the greatest Tao is extremely simple.*

Tao is the Ultimate Creator and Source. Tao carries Source love and light. Tao carries Source frequency and vibration. Tao carries Source most-positive information, energy, and matter, which could transform any and all negative information, energy, and matter in every aspect of life. Tao has infinite abilities. Tao carries the highest power of *soul over matter*, which is soulfulness. Soul over matter means *soul can make things happen.* Soul can transform every aspect of life, including health, relationships, finances, and the spiritual journey.

Another important ancient Chinese phrase is shu yi zai Dao 书以载道. This means *calligraphy is used to carry Tao.*

This book, *Tao Calligraphy to Heal and Rejuvenate Your Back*, will apply shu yi zai Dao through Tao Calligraphy Transformative Art. This unique form of Chinese calligraphy carries a Tao Source field, which is Tao Source frequency and vibration, to serve humanity and Mother Earth.

I will also introduce the universal law that is the law of creation, healing, transformation, and enlightenment for every aspect of life. This law of creation is the soul over matter information system governing everyone and everything.

I will share the ten greatest qualities carried within Tao Calligraphy Transformative Art to transform and enlighten all life.

I wish this book will serve you to transform challenges in your life.

I wish this book will serve you to transform challenges in your family.

I wish this book will serve humanity to transform challenges in society.

I wish this book will serve countless souls to transform challenges for cities, countries, and Mother Earth.

I love my heart and soul
I love all humanity
Join hearts and souls together
Love, peace, and harmony
Love, peace, and harmony

Universal Law of Shen Qi Jing: A Soul Over Matter Information System

THERE IS GREAT ancient wisdom within three words: jing qi shen 精氣神. The *Yellow Emperor's Inner Canon* 黃帝內經, the earliest authoritative book of traditional Chinese medicine, explains jing is *matter*; qi is *energy*; and shen is *soul* or *spirit*, which is expressed through energy and matter.

Everyone and everything are made of shen qi jing.[1] A human being, an animal, a house, an ocean, a mountain, Mother Earth, and countless planets, stars, galaxies, and universes are all made of shen qi jing.

Generally speaking, we can see matter and feel energy, but we cannot see the soul. For example, if we are on the shore by an ocean, we could feel the ocean's energy. If we are on a mountain, we could feel the mountain's energy. Under

---

[1] I reverse the traditional order of jing qi shen to shen qi jing because, as I will explain, the soul is the boss.

the sun, we can feel the sun's energy. However, most people cannot see the soul of an ocean, a mountain, or the sun because the soul is a light being. A soul's light is beyond the spectrum of visible light. Even a highly-developed spiritual being with open spiritual channels may not be able to see souls.

Dr. Rulin Xiu, a quantum physicist and string theorist, co-founded Tao Science[2] with me. Tao Science shares that shen qi jing is a universal law, just as the Law of Yin Yang and the Law of Five Elements are universal laws, which means that they apply to and describe everyone and everything in countless planets, stars, galaxies, and universes.

The Universal Law of Shen Qi Jing is the first foundational law of Tao Science. This law states that:

**Everyone and everything are
made of shen, qi, and jing.**

Shen includes soul, heart, and mind. This heart is more than the physical heart. This heart is the core of life.

Qi is energy.

Jing is matter.

Because energy and matter make up the body, we can re-state the Law of Shen Qi Jing as follows:

---

[2] See Zhi Gang Sha and Rulin Xiu, *Tao Science: The Science, Wisdom, and Practice of Creation and Grand Unification* (Cardiff, California/Richmond Hill, Ontario: Waterside Press/ Heaven's Library Publication Corp., 2017).

Everyone and everything have a
soul, heart, mind, and body.

Einstein's renowned equation, $E = mc^2$, states the relationship between the energy (E) and mass (m) of a body of matter. Tao Science states the relationship among soul, energy, and matter via the equation:

$$S + E + M = 1$$

In this equation, "S" represents shen, which includes soul, heart, and mind.

"E" represents qi or energy.

"M" represents jing or matter.

"1" represents the Tao Source Oneness Field.

Dr. Rulin Xiu and I feel that the Tao Source Oneness Field is the grand unified field that physicists have been seeking for decades in order to develop a grand unification theory that encompasses all known fields and forces in space and time. I will explain the Tao Source Oneness Field further in subsequent chapters.

The equation $S + E + M = 1$ expresses that one's soul, heart, and mind, plus energy and matter, are in a Oneness field. If this Oneness field is broken, then any challenges in all life could appear, whether in health, relationships, finances, the spiritual journey, or any other aspect.

To heal, transform, and enlighten every aspect of life is to align one's soul, heart, mind, energy, and matter as one. This is a universal law and the ultimate truth for all life.

The Law of Shen Qi Jing Is a Law of Creation

In this book some major wisdom, concepts, and practices are emphasized and repeated. The purpose is to help you realize their importance and to imprint them in your heart and soul.

Shen includes soul, heart, and mind. Soul is information or message. The Law of Shen Qi Jing describes a soul over matter information system. This soul over matter information system describes the process of creation, which has five steps.

Five Steps of Creation

The five steps of creation are:

Step 1. Soul is information, which is a creator.

The concept and study of information are key in quantum physics and Tao Science. In simple terms, if we think of everyone and everything as a computer network, information is like the data input that determines the output, including the characteristics, behavior, and nature of a system.

In spiritual terms, information or message is soul. For everyone and everything, the soul is the warehouse of information. For example, a person's soul is the warehouse of all the information or messages the person has accumulated in current and past lifetimes.

The information stored by the soul is a creator. "Soul over matter" means *the soul can make things happen*. In fact, the soul can transform every aspect of life.

Step 2. Soul leads the heart.

Everyone and everything have a heart. This heart is more than the physical heart. This heart is the physical heart, the emotional heart, the spiritual heart, and more. A human has a heart. An animal has a heart. Does an ocean have a heart? Does a mountain have a heart? Does Mother Earth have a heart? Yes! They all have a heart. This heart is the receiver of the information stored by the soul. This heart is the core of life.

Step 3. Heart leads the mind.

Mind is consciousness. It includes superficial consciousness, deep consciousness, subconsciousness, logical consciousness, imaginal consciousness, inspirational consciousness, huge consciousness, and more.

Consciousness is a big subject to study. Millions of people apply mind over matter, which is mindfulness. This means the mind can make things happen. Millions of people meditate. Millions of people use positive thinking.

Millions of people use positive chanting, such as affirmations. These practices all belong to mind over matter or mindfulness.

Mind is the processor. Think about a factory. In the chain of production, raw or unassembled material is input. At the end of the chain, the output is the finished product. Similarly, the input that the mind receives is information or messages from the soul, via the heart. The mind processes this information, consciously or subconsciously, and then makes a decision—consciously or subconsciously—as its "finished product."

Mind over matter and mindfulness are great. But in my personal opinion, they are not enough. People may not be aware that mindfulness is directed by the heart. We could move to heart over matter or heartfulness. Heartfulness would be a level beyond mindfulness. In ancient wisdom, the heart houses the mind and soul. The ultimate level is soulfulness, which is soul over matter. Soul over matter is the core teaching in all of my books and I apply it in all of the practices I share.

Step 4. Mind leads energy.

Energy is the mover. Energy drives matter. In the human body, energy drives blood. One fundamental tenet of traditional Chinese medicine since its inception five thousand years ago is:

> **If qi (energy) flows, blood flows.**
> **If qi is blocked, blood is stagnant.**

In the understanding of traditional Chinese medicine, all cysts, tumors, and cancers are due to qi blockages. There is an ancient statement:

qi ju ze cheng xing, qi san ze cheng feng
氣聚則成形, 氣散則成风

Qi means *energy*. Ju means *to accumulate*. Ze is a conjunction indicating causation. Cheng means *to become*. Xing means *shape*. Qi ju ze cheng xing means *qi accumulates to form a shape*. This is how a cyst, a tumor, and cancer are formed.

San means *to disperse*. Feng means *wind*. Qi san ze cheng feng means *qi disperses like the wind flowing away*.

Millions of people meditate. Meditation is at the mind level. Mind directs energy. For example, if in your meditation you focus on your kidneys, your energy will move toward the kidneys. Mind leads energy.

Step 5. Energy leads matter.

Blood is matter. If energy flows, blood flows. If a person sprains an ankle, the skin, muscles, tendons, and even the bones around the ankle could be injured. The blood is stagnant. Blood stagnation causes pain and makes movement difficult.

Matter manifests the information in our physical reality. It can transform the information.

Figure 1 summarizes the five steps of creation in the Universal Law of Shen Qi Jing.

Figure 1. Universal Law of Shen Qi Jing: Five Steps of Creation

The five steps of creation from the Law of Shen Qi Jing are vital for every aspect of life. More than sixteen years ago, on Saturday, September 10, 2005, I was with three of my trained soul-healing teachers and healers at Muir Woods National Monument just north of San Francisco. There, I asked the Divine directly, "Dear Divine, could you give me a song for healing?"

Instantly I could see with my spiritual eye a beam of rainbow light flowing down from Heaven into and through my whole body, from head to toe. Then, I opened my mouth. The following sounds flowed out:

Lu La Lu La Li
Lu La Lu La La Li
Lu La Lu La Li Lu La
Lu La Li Lu La
Lu La Li Lu La

I knew right away this was the Divine's soul voice and language. The Divine told me that he is giving me one of his songs and with that I received the melody.

I asked the Divine to give me the meaning of this soul language and song. I received a translation in Chinese, my native language, first:

wo ai wo xin he ling 我愛我心和靈
wo ai quan ren lei 我愛全人类
wan ling rong he mu shi sheng 萬靈融合睦世生
xiang ai ping an he xie 相愛平安和谐
xiang ai ping an he xie 相愛平安和谐

Let me explain line by line.

wo ai wo xin he ling
Wo means *I* or *my*. Ai means *to love*. Xin means *heart*. He means *and*. Ling means *soul*. Wo ai wo xin he ling means *I love my heart and soul.*

wo ai quan ren lei
Quan means *entire*. Ren lei means *humanity*. Wo ai quan ren lei means *I love all humanity.*

wan ling rong he mu shi sheng
Wan ling means *all souls*. Rong he means *meld as one*. Mu shi means *harmonious world*. Sheng means *to create* or *to give birth to*. Wan ling rong he mu shi sheng means *all souls meld as one to create a harmonious world.*

xiang ai ping an he xie

Xiang ai means *love*. Ping an means *peace*. He xie means *harmony*. Xiang ai ping an he xie means *love, peace, harmony*.

Then, the Divine gave me the English translation to be sung to his melody:

I love my heart and soul
I love all humanity
Join hearts and souls together
Love, peace, and harmony
Love, peace, and harmony

The Divine Soul Song "Love, Peace, and Harmony" has created hundreds of thousands of heart-touching and amazing results for healing and transformation, including for health, relationships, finances, the spiritual journey, and every aspect of life.

This Divine Soul Song explains and embodies the five steps of creation from the Law of Shen Qi Jing very well.

Step 1. Soul is information or message, which is a creator.

The process of soul over matter is: soul leads heart; heart leads mind; mind leads energy; energy leads blood, which is matter.

Every line, every word of this Divine Soul Song is information. The entire Divine Soul Song is a powerful accumulation of the positive information of each line.

I love my heart and soul
I love all humanity
Join hearts and souls together
Love, peace, and harmony
Love, peace, and harmony

This information is a creator.

Step 2. Soul leads the heart.

Soul passes the information or message to the heart. The heart is the receiver of the information. When we sing or even listen to this Divine Soul Song, our heart receives its information or message. The more open and clear our heart is, the more fully and deeply our heart will receive the information or message of "Love, Peace, and Harmony."

Step 3. Heart leads the mind.

Our heart passes the information or message to our mind. The mind receives the information or message and processes it.

Step 4. Mind leads energy.

The mind then passes the information to our energy. The energy moves.

Step 5. Energy leads matter.

Energy moves matter. Matter transforms. Blood is matter. Energy drives blood to flow more fluidly. Then, we are healing and transforming.

The Law of Shen Qi Jing is a law of creation that can explain any creation process. I am delighted to release this new wisdom that the Universal Law of Shen Qi Jing is a law of creation for humanity and Mother Earth.

The Law of Shen Qi Jing is a Law of Healing, Transformation, and Enlightenment

The Universal Law of Shen Qi Jing is also a law of healing, transformation, and enlightenment.

I released the Say Hello soul-healing technique sixteen years ago in my book, *Soul Mind Body Medicine*.[3] Twelve years ago, I traveled to India to teach soul healing. In one of my workshops, a medical doctor came to the stage and shared two soul-healing stories from his patients.

The first story was about a woman who had suffered from serious psoriasis for seven years. Her whole body was inflamed and shedding dry, flaky skin. The doctor, a family physician, guided this woman to do my Say Hello soul-healing practice. He taught her to say:

> *Dear soul, mind, and body of my skin,*
> *I love you.*
> *You have the power to heal yourself.*
> *Do a good job!*
> *Thank you.*

---

[3] Zhi Gang Sha, *Soul Mind Body Medicine: A Complete Soul Healing System for Optimum Health and Vitality* (Novato, California: New World Library, 2006).

This woman repeated this Say Hello soul-healing formula, which I named Soul Power—the power of soul over matter—from morning to night. Within two days, the inflammation was completely gone. Within seven days, the skin on her whole body was cleared and returned to a normal appearance. This doctor was so impressed that he immediately purchased all of my available books at that time, saying he was eager to read all of them.

The Say Hello soul-healing technique is soul over matter.

The doctor's second story was about a woman who suffered from a large mass (about five inches across) on her uterus. The physician also told her to repeat the Say Hello soul-healing technique and formula:

Dear soul, mind, and body of my uterus,
I love you.
You have the power to heal yourself.
Do a good job!
Thank you.

This woman repeated the Say Hello formula for a total of more than two hours a day.

I have taught for decades that people who suffer from chronic pain or life-threatening conditions need to do soul-healing practices for at least two hours per day. There is no time limit. The longer one practices, the better the results one could receive. Practice can be done in shorter segments. I recommend at least twenty minutes per practice session. For very serious and life-threatening conditions, total daily practice time (in however many individual practice sessions) should be at least two hours.

The woman with the uterine tumor practiced for two hours or more a day. After three weeks, her tumor disappeared. The physician said in my workshop that he could hardly believe what had happened for the two women just by repeating the Say Hello soul-healing formula.

These two stories demonstrate that the Universal Law of Shen Qi Jing is also a law of healing and transformation. How? It is easy to understand. The five steps of creation in the Universal Law of Shen Qi Jing can create healing and transformation.

Step 1. Soul is information or message, which is a creator.

The Say Hello soul-healing technique and formula is the information that is a creator.

Step 2. Soul leads the heart.

Every skin cell has a soul. Every skin cell has a heart. Every uterine tumor cell has a soul. Every uterine tumor cell has a heart. The hearts of the skin, skin cells, uterus, uterus cells, uterine tumor, and uterine tumor cells receive the healing information of the Say Hello soul-healing technique. The hearts of the cells pass the information to the minds or consciousness of the skin and uterus cells.

Step 3. Heart leads the mind.

Every cell of the skin, uterus, and uterine tumor has a mind. The minds of the cells receive the healing information from the hearts of the cells. The minds process and then pass the information to the energy.

Step 4. Mind leads energy.

The energy receives the healing information from the minds and moves. This energy movement drives the matter.

Step 5. Energy leads matter.

Blood is matter. The energy drives the blood. Blood flows better. All the biochemical behavior in the body could transform at the cellular level. The matter of the skin and the uterine tumor could transform at the cellular level. Thus, the two women recovered completely in a short time.

Humanity suffers from many sicknesses. Soul-healing techniques, which are soul over matter, apply the Universal Law of Shen Qi Jing as a law of creation, as a law of healing and transformation, and as a law of enlightenment (because it can heal and transform one's spiritual journey). We have received literally thousands of heart-touching and moving results from those applying the Say Hello soul-healing and transformation technique for healing of the physical body, emotional body, mental body, and spiritual body, as well as for transforming relationships and finances.

Peter Hudoba, a medical doctor and neuroscientist, has led numerous clinical research studies on a total of more than six hundred subjects on the effects of soul-healing techniques, including Tao Source soul healing, for various conditions. Chapter eleven shares some of the essence of this medical research.

2

Tao Science Explains the Universal Law of Shen Qi Jing

DR. RULIN XIU and I co-created Tao Science in 2016. Dr. Xiu is a quantum physicist and string theorist, having received her Ph.D. in 1994 from the University of California at Berkeley. She is also an entrepreneur, herbalist, singer, author, and a Master Teacher and Healer trained by my Tao Academy and me. Tao Science is the culmination of her three decades of work on a grand unification theory.

Tao is the Source of everyone and everything. Tao Science is the science of the Source, creation, healing, transformation, and enlightenment. Tao Science is a new groundbreaking science that helps unify science and spirituality at the most fundamental level. Tao Science is the science of grand unification.

According to ancient Chinese wisdom, which is part of the Universal Law of Shen Qi Jing, everyone and everything are made of three things: shen (soul, heart, and mind), qi (energy), and jing (matter).

Scientific research reveals that these three basic constituents of everyone and everything—shen, qi, and jing—generally correspond to three scientific concepts: information, energy, and matter.

Matter is what we see, hear, feel, observe, and experience. It is everything in our physical reality.

Energy is what changes and moves matter.

Information is what determines the form and shape of matter and energy. It is that which informs. To inform is to answer a question. Questions can be posed so that the answer is either "yes" or "no." Therefore, information can be represented as a sequence of yesses and nos. A computer does exactly this by specifying information using a series of 0s and 1s. Living in the information age, we know the importance of this. For example, we know that the information about our bank account determines how much money we can withdraw from it.

Modern physics reveals that everyone and everything is a vibrational field. A vibration, also called a wave, is a periodic oscillation extending over space and time. A vibration is described by its frequency, wavelength, amplitude, and velocity. Frequency describes how fast the vibration oscillates. Wavelength is the distance between two adjacent peaks of the vibration. Amplitude tells us the height of the oscillation. Velocity shows the speed at which the vibration travels. Our vibrational field contains many different vibrations. It carries information, energy, and matter.

Although everything we observe and experience is matter, it takes energy to move and change matter, and it is information that determines energy and matter. Information determines and creates what we observe and experience. Information in our vibrational field determines every aspect of our life.

Information consists of three aspects: content of information, receiver and emitter of information, and processor of information.

We find that the content of information in our vibrational field is spirit or soul. Because the content of information determines every aspect of life, spirit or soul is the essence of our life. It plays a critical role in shaping our life. When our physical body ceases to function, the content of information in our vibrational field still exists. That is why our spirit or soul continues its journey even when our physical life ends.

Physical life is limited. Spirit or soul can be eternal. Physical life is determined and directed by the spirit or soul. The highest purpose of our physical life is to serve our soul's purpose. Our soul has its purpose. When we know our soul's purpose, our physical life can be smoother and have greater meaning and impact.

We have a physical heart and a spiritual heart. The spiritual heart is the heart mentioned in spiritual writings. We have discovered that the spiritual heart is the receiver and emitter of information. The antenna of a radio is a receiver of information. It can receive the vibrations and information of a radio program transmitted from a radio station, making it possible for us to hear the broadcast. Similarly, our spiritual heart, the receiver and emitter of information, makes it possible to manifest the information from our soul into our reality. Without applying our spiritual heart, we would not be able to receive all of the positive information from our soul to empower us to manifest a life we want.

Mind is the processor of information. Similar to a computer, our mind can process information received from our spiritual heart. The output of this process is a decision, which could be conscious or subconscious. With this decision, the mind tells us what action to take. In this way, mind directs energy and changes the matter, our physical reality.

In our research, we have discovered that there are two kinds of information: positive and negative.

Positive information describes the connection, order, and harmony existing within someone or something and with others. Positive information gives a soul the power to create simply by giving a message. Positive information brings health, longevity, peace, efficiency, good relationships, abundant finances, and success in every aspect of life. A happy, healthy, and successful life is built on a solid foundation of positive information. Therefore, the purpose of life is to enhance our positive information.

Negative information is the disconnection, disorder, and disharmony within someone or something and with others. Negative information generates sickness, unbalanced emotions, inefficiency, difficulties in relationships, blockages in finances, and lack of success in any aspect of life. Negative information is the root cause of all diseases, misfortune, and challenges in life.

In one sentence:

**Information is the root cause of
success and failure in any aspect of life.**

Positive information is the root cause of success. Negative information is the root cause of failure. Therefore, to heal, transform, empower, and uplift our life at the deepest root level is to turn negative information in our vibrational field into positive information.

Everyone and everything are an information system. Our soul, heart, and mind are three important aspects of our information system, which molds every aspect of our life. From the point of view of information, energy is the actioner of information. Matter is the manifester and transformer of information. Our physical life is the manifestation of our soul's information. What we experience in our life and how we experience it tells our soul the consequences of the information it carries through our heart, mind, and body. The purpose of our physical life is to help our soul learn, transform, and be uplifted to a higher level of positive information.

When we give a specific message or information, the specific information starts to attract and direct energy and matter and leads to the phenomena we observe and experience. This is how we create our own reality and our own life.

The Law of Shen Qi Jing is a law of cause and effect. Information, including soul, heart, and mind, is the cause. Our physical reality is the effect of the information. This tells us how we ourselves create every aspect of our life from the information we give and receive through thinking, feeling, speaking, hearing, seeing, writing, and other actions.

If we want to create a life we truly want, we should be disciplined to think, feel, speak, hear, see, write, and convey the proper information, which is positive information or positive messages, about what we want in life. If we think, feel, speak, hear, see, write, and convey information about what we don't want, which is negative information, we will experience what we don't want. This is why we need to stop thinking, feeling, speaking, hearing, seeing, writing, and doing things that convey information about what we don't want.

Five sacred phrases tell us to avoid receiving and creating negative information:

mu bu wang shi 目不妄视
er bu wang ting 耳不妄听
kou bu wang yan 口不妄言
nao bu wang xiang 脑不妄想
xin wu gua ai 心无挂碍

These mean:

Eyes do not see negative things.
Ears do not hear negative words or sounds.
Mouth does not speak negative words.
Mind does not think negative thoughts.
Heart is not concerned or disturbed.

Buddha taught "xin wu gua ai" 心无挂碍. Xin means *heart*. Wu means *not*. Gua ai means *to be concerned* or *to worry*. All concerns and worries convey negative information, which creates the reality of what we worry about. When our heart does not have any concerns, worries, fears, grief, anger, sense of lack, depression, or any negativity, we can create and enjoy a life we want. Xin wu gua ai is important wisdom and a practice to create a life we want.

ॐ ॐ ॐ

The source of everyone and everything is emptiness. In physics, emptiness is called a vacuum. Emptiness has no shape or form. It has no space or time. Quantum physics tells us that within a vacuum or emptiness there are infinite possibilities and infinite information, energy, and matter. Everyone and everything come from the Source.

Source is connected with everyone and everything. This is why Source has pure positive information, energy, and matter.

The beauty and power of this book come from connecting with a Tao Source field to receive Source frequency and vibration; Source most-positive information, energy, and matter; and Source highest power of soul over matter to heal and transform our negative fields of negative information, energy, and matter.

Why Do People Have Challenges in Health, Relationships, Finances, and Every Aspect of Life?

MILLIONS OF PEOPLE suffer from sickness in the physical body, including all kinds of pain, inflammation, cysts, tumors, cancer, COVID-19, and many other sicknesses.

Millions of people suffer from sickness in the emotional body, including anger, depression, anxiety, worry, grief, fear, guilt, shame, loneliness, and more.

Millions of people suffer from sickness in the mental body, including poor concentration, diminishing memory, negative thinking, judgment, ego, and many mental disorders, such as schizophrenia, OCD, PTSD, and more.

Millions of people suffer from sickness in the spiritual body, because the soul can carry negative information. In fact, as we have seen in the Universal Law of Shen Qi Jing, negative information is the root cause of all kinds of sickness in the physical, emotional, mental, and spiritual bodies.

Millions of people have relationship challenges, including with partners, parents, children, siblings, other relatives, friends, bosses, employees, colleagues, organizations, and more.

Organizations, belief systems, cities, countries, and more could also have relationship challenges with each other.

Millions of people have environmental challenges, including polluted air, water, or land, inadequate shelter, unhealthy food, lack of healthcare, and more.

Millions of people have financial challenges.

Why do we have so many challenges in every aspect of life?

What is the key to understanding all of these challenges?

Is there a solution for these challenges?

If so, what is the solution?

I wrote this book to answer these four questions. Above all, I wrote this book to serve you, humanity, and Mother Earth.

In one sentence:

Humanity has all kinds of challenges in health, relationships, finances, the spiritual journey, and every aspect of life because of negative information, energy, and matter (negative shen qi jing).

What is the key to understanding all of these challenges? In one sentence, the key is that the heart and the soul are affected and influenced by negative information, energy, and matter.

Is there a solution for these challenges? In one sentence, the solution to all challenges in health, relationships, finances, the spiritual journey, and every aspect of life is to apply positive information, energy, and matter (positive shen qi ing) to transform negative information, energy, and matter.

Positive Information, Energy, and Matter

Tao Science states that information, energy, and matter can be positive or negative. This revolutionary insight helps us deeply understand sickness, healing, and transformation. What are positive information, energy, and matter? Positive information, energy, and matter are any information, energy, or matter that promotes order, connection, and harmony. Positive information, energy, and matter can heal and transform sickness, prevent sickness, rejuvenate, prolong life, harmonize relationships, boost finances and business, and enlighten one's spiritual journey.

There are ten qualities that carry the most-positive information, energy, and matter: greatest love, greatest forgiveness, greatest compassion, greatest light, greatest humility, greatest harmony, greatest flourishing, greatest gratitude, greatest service, and greatest enlightenment. I will explain these ten greatest qualities in more detail in chapter eight.

Because these ten greatest qualities are the most-positive information, energy, and matter, they can transform every aspect of life. They are the highest wisdom. At the same time, they are the highest practice. They carry the highest power.

In ancient wisdom, shu yi zai Dao 书以载道, which means *calligraphy is used to carry Tao*. In this book, I share two Tao Calligraphies I have written to carry some of the ten greatest qualities to serve you, as well as to serve families, humanity, organizations, cities, countries, and Mother Earth.

Tao Calligraphy is Tao Source Oneness writing. It is art. It is art beyond art that can heal and transform health, relationships, finances, the spiritual journey, and every aspect of life. I will teach you how to practice in the Tao Calligraphy Field to transform every aspect of life. The practices are simple but profound. Practice is vital for you to receive the greatest possible benefits that I wish you and every reader to receive.

In one sentence:

All good health, harmonious relationships, flourishing finances and business, and enlightened spiritual journeys are due to positive information, energy, and matter.

Negative Information, Energy, and Matter

What are negative information, energy, and matter? Negative information, energy, and matter are any information, energy, or matter that promotes disorder, disconnection, and disharmony. Negative information, energy, and matter cause sickness, relationship challenges, and financial challenges. Negative information, energy, and matter block one's spiritual journey. Negative information, energy, and matter create blockages in every aspect of life.

A human being has physical, emotional, mental, and spiritual bodies.

In the physical body, any lack of energy, vitality, or stamina; any pain, inflammation, cysts, tumors, or cancer; and all other sicknesses are negative information, energy, and matter.

In the emotional body, anger, depression, anxiety, guilt, shame, worry, grief, fear, and more are negative information, energy, and matter.

In the mental body, confusion, mental disorders, poor concentration, poor memory, ego, and more are negative information, energy, and matter.

In the spiritual body, not understanding or realizing the importance of the soul journey, which is the spiritual journey, getting lost on one's spiritual journey, creating mistakes of hurting and harming others and the environment, and more are negative information, energy, and matter.

For relationships, any disharmony in any kind of relationship is negative information, energy, and matter.

For finances, all blockages in any aspect of finances are negative information, energy, and matter.

For a business, any challenge in any part of the business is negative information, energy, and matter.

In one sentence:

All challenges, blockages, and failures in health, relationships, finances, and the spiritual journey are due to negative information, energy, and matter.

How to Transform Negative Information, Energy, and Matter

To transform all challenges in health, relationships, finances, the spiritual journey, and every aspect of life is to transform negative information, energy, and matter to positive information, energy, and matter.

I am delighted to offer a Tao Source practical tool to help you, families, society, organizations, humanity, and Mother Earth. This practical tool is named Tao Calligraphy.

Tao Calligraphy creates and carries an Ultimate Source most-positive field, which could transform negative fields in all life, including health, relationships, finances, and the spiritual journey. Health includes four bodies: physical, emotional, mental, and spiritual. I continue to explain the Tao Calligraphy Field in the next chapter.

Field

T HE ENGLISH PHYSICIST and chemist Michael Faraday coined the term "field" in 1849.

Scientists and others have identified and studied many kinds of fields, such as:

- electric
- magnetic
- electromagnetic
- gravitational
- temperature
- velocity flow
- quantum
- and more

In 1920, Albert Einstein realized that the concept of field, specifically a gravitational field, is a more accurate way to describe gravity than as a force. Finally, Einstein emphasized that there is only one real thing in the universe, which is a field.

Quantum physics discovered that everyone and everything is fundamentally a vibrational field made of various vibrations. A vibration, also called a wave, is a periodic oscillation extending over space and time. Quantum physics further reveals that our vibrational field determines our qualities and life experiences. To be a person of good quality and to experience a good life, we need to have a good vibrational field.

A good vibrational field is one carrying positive information, energy, and matter. Positive information, energy, and matter bring connection, order, and harmony. They are the cause of good health, harmonious relationships, and success in finances and careers. A bad vibrational field is one carrying negative information, energy, and matter. Negative information, energy, and matter bring disconnection, disorder, and disharmony. They are the cause of sickness, difficulties, challenges, and disasters.

To transform negative information, energy, and matter in one's vibrational field to positive information, energy, and matter is to heal sickness, overcome adversity, and turn lack into abundance at the root level.

Tao is the Ultimate Creator and Source. The vibrational field of Tao Source contains unlimited positive information, energy, and matter. Tao Source can create anything. It can provide for, support, and nourish everyone and everything. To connect with the Source vibrational field is the highest and most powerful way to heal, transform, and empower ourselves.

This book shares with humanity that the Tao Calligraphy Field is a Tao Source field, that the Tao Calligraphy Field exists, and that the Tao Calligraphy Field is available to serve you now.

In chapter one, I explained the Universal Law of Shen Qi Jing, which is a law of creation, a law of healing, a law of transformation, and a law of enlightenment. Shen qi jing form a field.

A human being is made of shen qi jing, which is soul, heart, mind, energy, and matter. A human being's shen qi jing form a human being's field.

An ocean is made of shen qi jing, which form an ocean's field.

Mother Earth is made of shen qi jing, which form Mother Earth's field.

A solar system has its own shen qi jing, which form a solar system's field.

In summary:

Everyone and everything in countless planets, stars, galaxies, and universes are made of their own shen qi jing. Their own shen qi jing form their own field.

Countless planets, stars, galaxies, and universes have both positive and negative shen qi jing, which are their positive and negative fields.

Positive Field

Any field that brings good health, harmonious relationships, flourishing finances, progress on the spiritual journey, or love, peace, and harmony to humanity, Mother Earth, and countless planets, stars, galaxies, and universes is a positive field.

Negative Field

Any field that causes unhealthy conditions for humanity, unharmonious relationships, blockages in finances, challenges on the spiritual journey, or reduces love, peace, and harmony for humanity, Mother Earth, and countless planets, stars, galaxies, and universes is a negative field.

The Universal Law of Shen Qi Jing tells us that positive shen qi jing could transform negative shen qi jing. In other words, a positive field could transform a negative field in health, relationships, finances, the spiritual journey, and every aspect of life.

How to Transform a Negative Field to a Positive Field

There are many ways to transform a negative field to a positive field.

In medicine, doctors, nurses, hospitals, and more help people to heal. They are transforming negative fields to positive fields.

People eat food and drink water. People realize that eating proper food and drinking healthy water are vital for life. When we do this, we are strengthening our positive field. We should avoid unhealthy foods and polluted water because they carry negative fields.

All kinds of education in every aspect of life are to teach about positive fields to empower students to transform negative fields. For example, positive education in science and technology tries to discover, develop, and apply positive fields to help humanity live healthier and happier lives in every aspect.

I honor all healing modalities and methods, all positive scientific and technological advances, and all the positive ways humanity has created and applied to transform negative information, energy, and matter to positive information, energy, and matter in every aspect of a human being's life.

I cannot emphasize enough that the purpose of this book is to introduce the Tao Calligraphy Field. This field is created by the transformative art of Tao Calligraphy, which carries a most-positive soul over matter information system to help humanity transform every aspect of life. Tao Calligraphy, which is Source Oneness transformative art, is a portal to (a) connect with Tao Source, (b) bring a Source field to humanity and Mother Earth, and (c) make it visible and tangible for healing, transformation, wisdom, nourishment, prosperity, success, and enlightenment in every aspect of life.

I will explain Tao, Tao Calligraphy, and the power and significance of Tao Calligraphy further in the next few chapters.

What Is Tao?

THE CONCEPT OF TAO was presented by Lao Zi, the ancient sage and author of *Dao De Jing*. In *Dao De Jing*, he explains Tao as the Ultimate Creator and Source and describes Tao Normal Creation.

Tao Normal Creation

Tao Normal Creation (figure 2) is explained in the first four sentences of chapter forty-two of *Dao De Jing*:

Dao sheng yi 道生一
Tao creates One.

Lao Zi explains that Tao is the Ultimate Source. Tao creates One, which is the Oneness world, called the Wu world. Wu 無 means *emptiness*. The Wu world cannot be seen, heard, or touched. It has no yin or yang, no space or time, no image or shape.

One, the Oneness world, is called hun yuan yi qi 混元一氣. Hun yuan means *blurred*. Yi means *oneness*. Qi means *energy*. There are two kinds of energy within the hun yuan yi qi. They are mixed and not separable, because hun yuan yi qi is blurred oneness energy. The two kinds of energy are named qing qi 清氣 and zhuo qi 浊氣. Qing qi is clean, pure, light qi. Zhuo qi is disturbed, turbid, heavy qi. They remain in the hun yuan yi qi condition for eons.

yi sheng er 一生二
One creates Two.

When the time comes for qi transformation, Tao separates the two qi in hun yuan yi qi, the Oneness world or blurred emptiness world. Qing qi (light, clean qi) rises to form Heaven. Zhuo qi (heavy, turbid qi) falls to form Mother Earth. Heaven and Earth are Two, which are the Yin Yang world.

Figure 2. Tao Normal Creation

er sheng san 二生三
Two creates Three.

Hun yuan yi qi, the Oneness world, plus Heaven and Earth, which are Two or the Yin Yang world, creates Three. Oneness plus Heaven and Earth are Three.

san sheng wan wu 三生萬物
Three creates all things.

Wan means *ten thousand*, which represents *infinite*, *countless*, or *all*. Wu means *things*. Wan wu is *all things*. Three, which is the Oneness world plus Heaven and Earth, creates all things in countless planets, stars, galaxies, and universes.

Tao Reverse Creation

I received the teaching of Tao Reverse Creation from Tao Source. Tao Source asked me to explain Tao Reverse Creation to humanity and all souls. See figure 3.

As with Tao Normal Creation, Tao Reverse Creation is also described in four sacred sentences:

wan wu gui san 萬物归三
All things return to Three. (Gui means *to return* or *to go back*.)

san gui er 三归二
Three returns to Two.

er gui yi 二归一
Two returns to One.

Figure 3. Tao Reverse Creation

yi gui Dao 一归道
One returns to Tao.

Together, Tao Normal Creation and Tao Reverse Creation are a universal law of universal reincarnation that explains how Tao creates One, Two, Three, and Wan Wu (all things), including countless planets, stars, galaxies, and universes, and how Wan Wu returns to Three, Two, One, and Tao, constantly and endlessly. See figure 4.

Tao Normal Creation and Tao Reverse Creation are profound. They are:

- highest wisdom
- highest philosophy

- highest science
- highest practice
- highest healing and transformation
- highest realization
- highest enlightenment
- ultimate truth

Tao Normal Creation and Tao Reverse Creation are sacred wisdom and ultimate truth that last for eons. Lao Zi was able to express Tao Normal Creation to humanity in *Dao De Jing*. It could take one decades or lifetimes to understand the profoundness and sacredness of Tao Normal Creation and Tao Reverse Creation. In one sentence:

Tao Normal Creation and Tao Reverse Creation are the ultimate creation and reincarnation circle for everyone and everything in countless planets, stars, galaxies, and universes.

Figure 4. Tao Normal Creation and Tao Reverse Creation

The Ultimate Creator and Source

I would like to explain chapter one of *Dao De Jing*. Chapter one succinctly summarizes the secret wisdom and profound power of the entire *Dao De Jing*.

道可道, 非常道
Dào kě dào, fēi cháng Dào

The Tao that can be expressed in words or comprehended by thoughts is not the permanent and true Tao.

Dào is Tao, the Ultimate Source.
Kě dào means *can be explained or can be comprehended*.
Fēi means *not*.
Cháng means *permanent*.

名可名, 非常名
míng kě míng, fēi cháng míng

Anyone and anything that can be named is not permanent.

Míng means *name*.
Kě means *to be able to*.
Fēi means *not*.
Cháng means *permanent*.

Anyone who has been given a name is not permanent because the human path is sheng lao bing si 生老病死 (*birth, old age, sickness, death*). The arc of life for everyone and everything is cheng zhu huai kong 成住坏空 (*grow and develop, remain stable, be damaged and diminish, disappear*). This is the path of everyone and everything in the Yin Yang world.

无名天地之始
wú míng tiān dì zhī shǐ

The condition with no name is the beginning of Heaven and Earth.

Wú means *no*.
Míng means *name*.
Tiān means *Heaven.*
Dì means *Mother Earth.*
Zhī is a possessive particle (equivalent to *'s*).
Shǐ means *beginning*.

The condition with no name is Tao. Tao creates One, which is the Wu (emptiness) world. Tao is emptiness. Tao also creates the You (existence) world, beginning with Heaven and Earth (Two) as I explained earlier in this chapter. Mother Earth is one planet. There are countless planets, stars, galaxies, and universes. Tao Source creates all of them, as well as Heaven, Mother Earth, and human beings.

有名万物之母
yǒu míng wàn wù zhī mǔ

The ones with names are the mother of wan wu (countless things).

Yǒu means *to exist* or *to have*.
Wàn means *ten thousand*. Ten thousand in Chinese represents *infinite* or *countless* or *all*.
Wù means *thing*.
Mǔ means *mother*.

Tian and di have names: *Heaven* and *Earth*. Tian di, Heaven and Earth, are the mu qin (mother) of everyone and everything. As Lao Zi explained in Tao Normal Creation, Heaven and Earth are Two. Two creates Three. Three creates everyone and everything.

故常无, 欲以观其妙
gù cháng wú, yù yǐ guān qí miào

Therefore, be permanently in the Wu condition, which is kong (emptiness). In this condition, one can observe the profound Tao without intention, restriction, or limitation.

Gù means *therefore*.

Cháng means *permanent*.

Wú means *emptiness*, which is Tao and yi (Oneness).

Yù yǐ guān qí miào means *to be able to observe the profoundness of Tao.*

When one reaches the qing jing 清靜 (pure, quiet, and peaceful) condition in the heart, then one can go into stillness (ding 定), which means no "me, me, me" and no thoughts. In this ding condition of forgetting oneself, one could observe the profoundness and sacredness of Tao. This is a very advanced spiritual condition that is not easy to achieve.

常有, 欲以观其徼
cháng yǒu, yù yǐ guān qí jiào

Be permanently in the You condition to observe the vastness of the You world. In this condition, one can observe the You world with intention, restrictions, and limitations.

Cháng means *permanent*.
Yǒu means *existence*.
Yù means *to desire* or *to be able to*.
Guān means *to observe*.
Qí refers to *Tao*.
Jiào means *boundary*.

To see Mother Earth and countless planets, stars, galaxies, and universes in the You world, a human's physical eyes, consciousness, and knowledge are not enough. Using the most advanced telescope, it still takes billions of years for the light from the farthest stars to reach our physical eyes. As vast as it is, the You world is limited. It has all kinds of restrictions and limitations.

此两者, 同出而异名, 同谓之玄
cǐ liǎng zhě, tóng chū ér yì míng, tóng wèi zhī xuán
These two (Wu and You worlds) both come from the same source (Tao), but have different names. Both are profound.

Cǐ means *these*.
Liǎng zhě means *two* (Wu and You worlds).
Tóng chū means *both come from Tao*.
Ér means *but*.
Yì míng means *different names*.
Tóng wèi zhī xuán means *both are profound, mysterious, sacred, and unimaginable*.

玄之又玄, 众妙之门
xuán zhī yòu xuán, zhòng miào zhī mén
The Wu and You worlds are both profound beyond profound, mysterious beyond mysterious, sacred beyond sacred, and

unimaginable beyond unimaginable—the gate to all sacred teachings and realms.

Xuán means *sacredness* or *profoundness*.
Yòu is used here to indicate a deeper meaning of xuán beyond the literal meaning of xuán.
Zhòng means *all*.
Miào means *profound, mysterious, sacred, or unimaginable.*
Zhī is a possessive particle, equivalent to 's in English.
Mén means *gate*.
Zhong miao zhi men means *the gate of all sacred wisdom, power, and realms.*

Lao Zi explained Tao in many chapters of *Dao De Jing*. Chapter one is the key to the profound wisdom and power of Tao. Allow me to summarize the concept of Tao:

- Tao cannot be explained by words or comprehended by thoughts.

- Tao cannot be seen, heard, or touched.

- Tao creates the Wu world and You world, which are the profound gates of wisdom, philosophy, science, culture, practice, and power for everyone and everything in countless planets, stars, galaxies, and universes.

- Tao has no yin, no yang, no time, no space, no image, no shape, no sound.

- Follow Tao, flourish. Go against Tao, end.

- Tao carries the ten greatest natures, which are Da Ai 大愛—Greatest Love, Da Kuan Shu 大寬恕—Greatest

Forgiveness, Da Ci Bei 大慈悲—Greatest Compassion, Da Guang Ming 大光明— Greatest Light, Da Qian Bei 大谦卑—Greatest Humility, Da He Xie 大和谐— Greatest Harmony, Da Chang Sheng 大昌盛— Greatest Flourishing, Da Gan En 大感恩—Greatest Gratitude, Da Fu Wu 大服务—Greatest Service, and Da Yuan Man 大圆满—Greatest Enlightenment.

- Tao expresses its ten greatest natures and powers as a Tao Source field.

- Tao carries Source most-positive information, energy, and matter (shen qi jing), which can transform negative information, energy, and matter.

- Tao is the Ultimate Creator, which is the highest soul. Therefore, Tao carries the highest soul power, which is *Tao over matter*. Tao over matter is the highest soul over matter. Soul over matter means soul can make things happen to help heal, transform, and enlighten all life. Tao over matter means Tao carries the highest power to heal, transform, and enlighten all life.

In one sentence:

Tao is The Way of all life.

What Is De?

De 德 is the shen kou yi 身口意 of Tao. This shen means *activities, actions, and behaviors*. Kou means *speech*. Yi means *thoughts*.

De is virtue, which is Source nutrients. A human receives human nutrients from fruits, vegetables, meat, and more, which carry vitamins, minerals, amino acids, proteins, and other essential nutrients.

Because de comes from Tao Source, it also carries Source nutrients, including Source liquids, vitamins, minerals, amino acids, proteins, nectars, and light. Human nutrients can be seen, tasted, touched, and felt. Source nutrients cannot be seen, tasted, touched, or felt.

Humanity has not realized enough that Tao Source nutrients are available. There is an ancient phrase that everyone should know: Dao sheng de yang 道生德养; *Tao creates, de nourishes.* The Tao Calligraphy Transformative Art Field brings Tao power with Tao Source nutrients to heal, prevent sickness, rejuvenate, nourish and prolong life, transform relationships and finances, enlighten the soul, and transform every aspect of life.

In one sentence:

De is Tao nutrients to nourish everyone and everything in countless planets, stars, galaxies, and universes.

The Power and Significance of Tao and De

Tao is the Ultimate Creator that constantly creates countless planets, stars, galaxies, and universes. Mother Earth is only one planet. Tao also creates human beings, animals, everyone, and everything. This is one of the top ancient wisdoms. It can be summarized in one sentence:

Tao creates and de nourishes countless planets, stars, galaxies, and universes, and everyone and everything, including human beings.

Tao is the universal principles and laws. Health has a Tao. Relationships have a Tao. Business and finances have a Tao. Education has a Tao. Every aspect of life has a Tao.

Tao is The Way of all life.

De, as Tao shen kou yi and Source nutrients, nourishes everyone and everything.

Tao and de exist in everyone and everything. There is an ancient philosophy and wisdom:

shun Dao chang, ni Dao wang 顺道昌, 逆道亡

This means *follow Tao, flourish; go against Tao, end* or *finish*. Everyone and everything in countless planets, stars, galaxies, and universes naturally follow this principle. Many people may not realize this.

In summary, Tao is the Ultimate Creator. De is Tao nutrients. Tao creates and de nourishes.

Tao is the universal principles and laws. Tao is The Way of all life. Tao is invisible. Lao Zi clearly explained in *Dao De Jing* that Tao cannot be seen, heard, or touched. Follow Tao, flourish. Go against Tao, end or finish.

This is to teach everyone that whether or not one realizes or believes in Tao, as the Ultimate Source it *is* guiding humanity, everyone, and everything. De as Source nutrients *is* nourishing humanity, everyone, and everything.

I have applied Tao and de wisdom and principles to create thousands of heart-touching and moving results for healing, harmonious relationships, and flourishing finances. We have completed scientific research on more than six hundred subjects to demonstrate the effectiveness and simplicity of Tao de service. (Some of our research results are presented in chapter eleven.) Tao Calligraphy Transformative Art is one of our most important tools for healing and transformation. I will explain Tao Calligraphy Transformative Art and lead you in practice so that you can experience its power and significance and receive its benefits.

Chinese Calligraphy

THE EARLIEST KNOWN written records in China date to the Shang Dynasty (1600–1046 BCE), specifically, to the reign of Emperor Wu Ding 武丁 in roughly the 13th century BCE. Records were kept in the emperor's palace through carvings on the underside of tortoise shells and on ox bones. These were also used by fortune tellers and even emperors themselves to make predictions; hence, they are also called "oracle bones." The symbols carved can be regarded as the earliest known Chinese character writing system and the mother of all subsequent Chinese script.

Chinese calligraphy is the art of writing Chinese characters. With painting, it is one of the most important ancient Chinese arts, gaining prominence and reverence during the Dong Han 东汉 (Eastern Han) Dynasty (25–220 CE).

Figure 5 below shows some of the evolution and different styles of Chinese calligraphy for six basic Chinese characters, from top to bottom: ri 日 (*sun*), yue 月 (*moon*), shan 山 (*mountain*), tian 田 (*field*), huo 火 (*fire*), and shui 水 (*water*).

Jia gu wen is the script used for oracle bones.

Figure 5. Evolution and Styles of Six Basic
Chinese Characters in Chinese Calligraphy

Jin wen ("metal script") was inscribed on ritual bronze vessels and other objects, mainly from the 13th century BCE to 770 BCE.

Xiao zhuan is the small seal script standardized by the Qin Dynasty c. 213 BCE. It is a simplified form of da zhuan, the great seal script used in the Zhou Dynasty c. 11th century BCE to 256 BCE. Da zhuan, also named zhou wen 籀 文, evolved directly from jin wen.

Li shu ("clerical script") was simplified from xiao zhuan ("small seal script") c. 200 BCE and became the official script in the Han Dynasty.

Kai shu is the "regular script" style of Chinese calligraphy, from c. 250 CE. Reaching its maturity c. 7th century CE, it is to this day the most common hanzi 汉字 (Chinese character) calligraphy script. It is also commonly used in print publications.

Xing shu is the "running script" style of Chinese calligraphy, from the 4th century CE.

Cao shu is the cursive script style of Chinese calligraphy, literally "grass script," from the 7th century CE.

Figure 6 shows these same six characters in Tao Calligraphy. I will explain Tao Calligraphy, Tao Source Oneness Transformative Art, in the next chapter.

Rì　　Yuè　　Shān　　Tián　　Huǒ　　Shuǐ

Figure 6. Six Basic Chinese Characters in Tao Oneness Calligraphy

Throughout its evolution and innovation over centuries, Chinese calligraphy has been a unique visual art that always radiates charm. The techniques and the philosophy of ancient Chinese calligraphy had a strong influence on Chinese painting. The two were even melded as one in many works.

The development of Chinese characters (hanzi) over three-and-a-half millennia is a vital element of Chinese calligraphy. This artform was created and developed as an integral part of Chinese culture and honored as one of the most important and prestigious arts in the culture. Therefore, we can say that Chinese characters are one of the fundamental elements of Chinese culture.

That Chinese calligraphy is based on Chinese characters differentiates it from other calligraphies. Chinese calligraphy is an expressive art originally created during the Qin 秦 (221–207 BCE) and Han 汉 (206 BCE–220 CE) dynasties. Chinese calligraphy is praised as "poetry without language or words," "dancing without movement," "painting without a picture," and "music without sound." The historian R. Dawson has written beautifully:

The printed characters are like figures in a Victorian photograph, standing stiffly to attention; but the brush-written ones dance down the pages with the grace and vitality of the ballet. The beautiful shapes of Chinese calligraphy were in fact compared with natural beauties, and every stroke was thought to be inspired by a natural object and to have the energy of a living thing. Consequently, Chinese calligraphers sought inspiration by watching natural phenomena.

Chinese calligraphy represents the extensive wisdom, knowledge, and profound scholarship of Chinese history and culture. It has become the symbol or signature of the Chinese nation.

What Is Tao Calligraphy?

I LEARNED TAO CALLIGRAPHY from the late Professor Li Qiuyun, who taught at the University of Toronto. She was honored by the United Nations as a global authority on the Chinese language. She studied in China under Tai Shi 太师, the "supreme teacher" of the family of the last emperor of China.

Professor Li was the sole lineage holder of a unique style of Chinese calligraphy named yi bi zi 一笔字, which means *one-stroke character*. In traditional regular script (also see the kai shu examples in Figure 5 on page 54), some characters are written with twenty, even thirty or more individual strokes. In yi bi zi, every character, no matter how many individual strokes it contains, is written in one continuous stroke of the brush. Even entire phrases consisting of multiple characters can be written in one continuous stroke.

I was extremely honored to become Professor Li's only lineage holder. After I learned yi bi zi, I put Tao Source power into my yi bi zi calligraphies for healing and transformation. The Tao Source power, including Source frequency and vibration, Source love and light, and Source

57

most-positive information, energy, and matter, transforms the yi bi zi calligraphy to Tao Calligraphy. Professor Li fully supported Tao Calligraphy and made a documentary film with me.

Now, I can explain Tao Calligraphy clearly. Tao Calligraphy is Source Oneness Transformative Art. Tao Calligraphy creates and carries a Tao Source Field. Tao exists in everyone and everything.

A Tao Calligraphy Field carries:

- the power of Tao, the Ultimate Creator and Source

- Source love and light. *Love melts all blockages. Light heals and transforms all life.*

- Source frequency and vibration, which can transform negative frequency and vibration for all life

- Source most-positive information, energy, and matter, which can transform negative information, energy, and matter for all life

- Source infinite capabilities

- Source highest power of soul over matter. *Soul can make things happen. Tao has the greatest power to make things happen.*

- a Source field to transform negative fields in all life.

Therefore, I call Tao Calligraphy "Source Oneness Transformative Art," "Tao Calligraphy Transformative Art," and more.

Tao Calligraphy Transformative Art Embodies the Ten Greatest Qualities to Transform and Enlighten Every Aspect of Life

I N THE INTRODUCTION I explained shu yi zai Dao, which means *calligraphy is used to carry Tao*. How does Tao Calligraphy do this? Tao Calligraphy Source Oneness Transformative Art carries the ten greatest qualities, which are ten Tao qualities. These ten greatest qualities can transform all life, including health, relationships, finances, and the spiritual journey.

How does Tao Calligraphy work? In one sentence:

Tao Calligraphy Transformative Art carries an Ultimate Creator and Source Field that could transform all life, including health, relationships, finances, and the spiritual journey.

Apply the Tao Calligraphy Transformative Art Field for healing the physical body.

Apply the Tao Calligraphy Transformative Art Field for healing the emotional body.

Apply the Tao Calligraphy Transformative Art Field for healing the mental body.

Apply the Tao Calligraphy Transformative Art Field for healing the spiritual body.

Apply the Tao Calligraphy Transformative Art Field for transforming all kinds of relationships.

Apply the Tao Calligraphy Transformative Art Field for transforming finances and business.

Apply the Tao Calligraphy Transformative Art Field for enlightening the spiritual journey.

Apply the Tao Calligraphy Transformative Art Field for healing, transforming, and enlightening every aspect of life.

I would like to share a heart-touching story about David Meltzer, a renowned speaker, author, and entrepreneur, and the benefits he has received from applying the Tao Calligraphy Transformative Art Field.

Please enjoy this brief video:

As David shares in the video, he has experienced great success in his life. He was a multimillionaire by the time he was thirty and became the CEO of the world's most notable sports agency, which was the inspiration and model for the movie, "Jerry Maguire."

Despite all of David's success, happiness was beyond his reach. After going through serious personal challenges, David says he learned a valuable lesson: you can't buy love or happiness.

David and I met about ten years ago through our mutual book agent, Bill Gladstone. David shared his initial response to meeting me:

I was extremely skeptical. I represented the greatest athletes, celebrities, and entertainers in the world, people who carried the spirit of excellence. It took a lot to get my attention when it came to vibration, frequency, or light. But once I met Dr. and Master Sha, I knew there was something special. There was a spirit of excellence and I wanted to be around it.

I gifted David two Tao Calligraphies and instructed him to trace them for ten minutes a day. David did this dedicatedly and his life started to change:

My life changed dramatically: my health, my relationships, my perspective, my mindset. I don't even know sometimes where the wisdom and enlightenment come from. People who have known me for years will comment as they watch the speeches and the books and TV shows and all the things that I am involved with and say, "When did you get so smart?"

Even though there is no logic or reason that would tell you that by tracing a piece of art on your wall your life would change, they work. I can tell you I don't know how it works. But I step on airplanes about two hundred days a year and I still don't know how an airplane flies, but I have faith every time I step on a plane that it's safer than driving my car home. I have faith in those calligraphies. My life has been impacted exponentially in every aspect: from health, happiness, wealth, and worthiness. What more can you ask for?

People come to me and say, "Mr. Meltzer, what can I do to change my life?" The first thing I tell them to do is to say 'thank you' before they go to bed and when they wake up. The next thing I tell them to do is to get a calligraphy from Master Sha and trace it. Both don't take very much time, and both have impacted my life more than anything else that I've ever done.

David Meltzer's original desire and request were for financial abundance. He received huge financial abundance within eighteen months of receiving and tracing the Tao Calligraphy *Dao Ye Chang Sheng* 道業昌盛 (*Tao career flourishes*) and he has continued to receive more and more. However, he also explained that he has received much more than financial abundance: improved family harmony, inspired wisdom, the ability to fulfill his greatest dream to serve humanity—all of this and more have totally transformed his life.

I wrote this book to serve you and all humanity through Tao Calligraphy. I deeply wish to see all humanity benefit from Tao Calligraphy. This is the first book in my Tao Calligraphy series. I will quickly write many more books.

Please see page 169 for the first ten books I have been guided to share with humanity in this book series.

Tao Calligraphy Source Oneness Transformative Art carries Tao natures and Tao powers. It carries the ten greatest natures and powers of Tao:

1. Da Ai 大愛—Greatest Love

2. Da Kuan Shu 大宽恕—Greatest Forgiveness

3. Da Ci Bei 大慈悲—Greatest Compassion

4. Da Guang Ming 大光明—Greatest Light

5. Da Qian Bei 大谦卑—Greatest Humility

6. Da He Xie 大和谐—Greatest Harmony

7. Da Chang Sheng 大昌盛—Greatest Flourishing

8. Da Gan En 大感恩—Greatest Gratitude

9. Da Fu Wu 大服务—Greatest Service

10. Da Yuan Man 大圆满—Greatest Enlightenment

I will explain each of these Ten Da (*greatest*) qualities in more detail.

Da Ai—Greatest Love:
Melts All Blockages and Transforms All Life

I received four sacred phrases about Da Ai, Greatest Love, from the Source:

yi shi da ai   一 施大愛
wu tiao jian ai   无条件愛

rong hua zai nan   融化灾难
xin qing shen ming   心清神明

一 施大愛 yi shi da ai
First give greatest love to humanity and all souls
Yi means *first*. Shi means *to give*. Da means *greatest*. Ai
means *love*.

无条件愛 wu tiao jian ai
Unconditional love
Wu means *no*. Tiao jian means *condition*.

融化灾难 rong hua zai nan
Melts all disasters, hardships, and challenges
Rong hua means *to melt*. Zai nan means *disasters, hardships, and challenges*.

心清神明 xin qing shen ming
Heart is pure and clean and soul, heart, and mind are enlightened
Xin means *heart*. Qing means *pure and clean*. Shen means *soul, heart, and mind*. Ming means *enlightened*.

Ancient spiritual wisdom teaches that the heart houses the mind and soul. Physical sicknesses are due to spiritual heart pollution, which includes greed; anger; lack of wisdom in activities, speech, and thoughts; doubt; ego; desire for fame or money; jealousy; competition; fighting nature; and more. These and other kinds of pollution in the spiritual heart are the true cause of sickness in the body. Millions of people are aware of this. Millions of people may not be aware of this. Therefore, to transform physical sickness, as well as to transform relationships and finances, one must transform one's spiritual heart. To transform the spiritual heart is to remove spiritual heart pollution, which is blockages in the spiritual heart.

Xin qing, a pure and clean heart, is a spiritual heart that has been cleansed of pollution or blockages.

Shen ming is an enlightened soul, heart, and mind.

Xin qing shen ming is first to cleanse the spiritual heart blockages. Then, enlightenment of one's soul, heart, and mind can follow.

What is enlightenment? To be enlightened is to be aware—specifically, to be aware of and to realize and embody the universal truths. Awareness is to understand that Tao Source is the Ultimate Creator that creates Heaven, Earth, and countless planets, stars, galaxies, and universes. Tao Source is The Way of all life.

Millions of people are searching for soul enlightenment, which means reaching this awareness. Millions of people may not be seeking enlightenment. People may not realize that xin qing shen ming—cleaning and purifying the spiritual heart and enlightening the soul, heart, and mind— could help one heal many sicknesses, solve many relationship and financial challenges, and make huge progress on the spiritual journey.

How can one achieve xin qing shen ming? Apply positive information, energy, and matter, which is a positive field, to transform the negative field of all kinds of spiritual heart pollution.

Tao Calligraphy creates and carries a Source field that could transform all kinds of spiritual pollution. Therefore, Tao Calligraphy could transform all life, including health, relationships, finances, and the spiritual journey, and finally help one reach soul, heart, and mind enlightenment.

In summary, the four sacred phrases about Da Ai tell us:

yi shi da ai	*First give greatest love to others and humanity*
wu tiao jian ai	*Unconditional love*
rong hua zai nan	*Melts all disasters and challenges*
xin qing shen ming	*Clean and purify the heart, enlighten the soul, heart, and mind*

Da Ai is the foundation of the Shi Da 十大. Shi means *ten*. Da means *greatest*. Shi Da or Ten Da are the ten greatest natures, qualities, and powers of Tao Source.

Da Ai is the greatest love. Greatest love is unconditional love. Greatest love is selfless love. To love unconditionally is to love without expecting anything in return. It is easy to say. It is difficult to do. But it is possible. Think about a human's life. Parents give love to their baby. Generally speaking, parents give their baby love unconditionally.

To give unconditional love is to love totally from one's heart and soul, without asking for anything in return. How can you give love unconditionally to others and to humanity? The key is to reduce "me, me, me." It is very

difficult for a self-centered or selfish person to give unconditional love.

Think about Heaven, Earth, the sun, and the moon. Do
they ask for anything in return for their nourishment, sus-
tenance, warmth, light, and more? They are all unconditional servants with unconditional love.

Millions of people honor Mother Mary. Millions of people
honor different saints and buddhas. Mother Mary and
other highest saints and buddhas carry unconditional
love. They have created countless heart-touching, moving, and miraculous results through healing and transformation in every aspect of life. Therefore, Da Ai, greatest
and unconditional love, carries unbelievable power to
transform all life, including health, relationships, finances,
and the spiritual journey.

In this book, I am further introducing a new way to carry
and apply Da Ai, greatest and unconditional love. This
new way is the Tao Calligraphy *Da Ai*. When I write the
Tao Calligraphy *Da Ai*, I connect with Tao Source. Tao
Source pours in Source love, which is the greatest love,
into the calligraphy. Therefore, the *Da Ai* Tao Calligraphy
carries a Source greatest love field. See figure 7.

Remember the wisdom I shared earlier: To transform any
aspect of life is to apply a positive field to transform a negative field. The Tao Source highest positive field carried
by Tao Calligraphy has unbelievable power to transform
every aspect of life.

Figure 7. Tao Calligraphy *Da Ai* (Greatest Love)

Hundreds of people have gathered online to experience my writing of the Tao Calligraphy *Da Ai*. As I write this Tao Calligraphy, I ask my leading teacher, Master Francisco Quintero, to do a spiritual reading:

As Master Sha prepares to write the Tao Calligraphy Da Ai, *he connects to Tao Source and many saints and buddhas in the spiritual realm. Then, as Master Sha touches his brush to the paper, each of these beings begins to pour their love and light into the Tao Calligraphy. As Master Sha continues to write, the light becomes brighter and brighter, forming a field of light that radiates in all directions. The calligraphy is transforming more and more from ordinary art to transformative art. It has become a Source healing field. The calligraphy is radiating bright golden light. The frequency and vibration are so pure. They have formed a Oneness field, carrying the unconditional love of countless saints and buddhas and the unconditional love of Tao Source.*

This Da Ai *Tao Calligraphy has such a high vibration that it instantly begins to cleanse blockages for all of us who are watching Master Sha create it. The love and light are nourishing our systems, organs, and cells, washing through the spaces and literally every cell. We are receiving a huge cleansing of our shen qi jing. This Tao Calligraphy is deeply healing and transforming all of us. It touches my heart deeply to observe these images in the spiritual realm. This calligraphy is sacred art.*

Now, I am asking everyone I have gathered online to request healing for one area of their body, which could be the physical, emotional, or mental body. You could request for a bodily system, an organ, a part of the body, or a condition. The condition could be physical, emotional, or mental, such as high blood pressure, migraines, COVID-19, depression, anger, a sore throat, shoulder pain, negative thinking, a cyst, a tumor, or cancer.

I then ask everybody to start to apply the Six Power Techniques, which are Body Power, Soul Power, Mind Power, Sound Power, Breathing Power, and Tao Calligraphy Power. I welcome you to join us in practice by following these instructions:

Apply the Six Power Techniques.

Body Power (using body and hand positions for healing)

Sit up straight. Keep your feet flat on the floor. Put one palm over your navel. Put the other palm over the area of the body where you are requesting healing and transformation. For example, for shoulder pain, place one palm on the painful shoulder.

Soul Power (soulfulness or "soul over matter" soul-healing technique, which I named Say Hello Healing and Transformation)

There are two ways to "say hello": say hello to inner souls and say hello to outer souls.

"Say hello" to inner souls:

> *Dear shen qi jing* (or soul, heart, mind, energy, and
>   matter) *of my* _____ (name the system, organ,
>   part of the body, or condition for which you are
>   requesting healing),

I love you.
You have the power to heal yourself.
Do a great job.
Thank you.

"Say hello" to outer souls:

Dear Tao Calligraphy Transformative Art Da Ai *Field,*
I love you, honor you, and appreciate you.
You are the Tao Source most-positive field.
You can transform the negative field of my _____ (say
   your request again).
Please heal and transform my _____ (repeat your
   request).
Thank you.

Repeat the Say Hello technique to inner souls and outer souls one more time.

In fact, there is no time limit for repeating the Say Hello soul-healing technique. For decades, thousands of heart-touching stories from around the world have proven the power of the Say Hello Healing and Transformation technique. I shared two of these stories on pp. 12–14.

Breathing Power

Life is breathing in and breathing out. If one does not breathe, there is no life. It is just like the heart beating. If the heart does not beat, there is no life also.

We all know that when a person breathes in, the body receives and absorbs oxygen. When a person breathes out, the body releases and expels carbon dioxide. Oxygen is needed by every cell in the body to transform nutrients and generate energy. With every breath one takes in, the life of every cell is being nourished and sustained. Carbon dioxide is a waste product of cellular metabolism. The cells release carbon dioxide and the blood transports it to the lungs, where it is expelled with every breath out.

I am delighted to share an ancient secret breathing technique for healing and transformation. It is named "xi qing hu zhuo" 吸清呼浊.

Xi means *to breathe in*. Qing means *positive information, energy, and matter*. Hu means *to breathe out*. Zhuo means *negative information, energy, and matter*.

As I explained, everyone and everything are made of shen qi jing. Everyone's and everything's shen qi jing creates a field. The Tao Calligraphy *Da Ai* creates and carries Source shen qi jing. Therefore, the Tao Calligraphy *Da Ai* carries a Source field.

The Tao Calligraphy *Da Ai*, Greatest Love, which is unconditional love, carries immeasurable power to transform negative shen qi jing, which form a negative field. When people connect with the Tao Calligraphy *Da Ai* Field, some could feel transformation instantly. Some people could take more time to feel better.

I am continuing the live demonstration online for hundreds of people. Each one, including you, dear reader, has made a request for healing and transformation of one aspect of the physical, emotional, or mental bodies. Let us continue to practice together now.

Follow my instructions:

Breathing Power and Tao Calligraphy Power together with Mind Power (creative visualization) and Sound Power (chanting sacred messages, sounds, or mantras)

Open the book to figure 7. Inhale deeply. As you inhale, you are receiving the positive frequency and vibration and the positive information, energy, and matter from the Tao Calligraphy *Da Ai* Field. Visualize this as golden light coming into the area where you requested healing by applying Soul Power above.

Now exhale. As you exhale, chant *Da Ai* (pronounced *dah eye*). This is Sound Power. The positive field of the Tao Calligraphy *Da Ai* will help you transform and release the negative field of your request, whether it was for relief from pain, inflammation, a cyst or tumor, cancer, or another physical sickness or disease, anger, anxiety, fear, or another emotional issue, or a mental issue such as negative thinking or poor concentration.

This is the ancient xi qing hu zhuo sacred breathing technique with the addition of Tao Calligraphy Power. We are breathing in the Tao Calligraphy *Da Ai* most-positive field and breathing out the negative field related to our request.

I am leading hundreds of people live to do this practice together for about twenty minutes. Please do it now so that you can also experience the power of the Tao Calligraphy Transformative Art Field. I always say: *If you want to know if a pear is sweet, taste it. If you want to know the power of the Tao Calligraphy Field, experience it.*

Practice

Connect with the Tao Calligraphy *Da Ai* Field in figure 7.

Breathe in. Visualize golden light bringing the Tao Calligraphy *Da Ai* Field to the area for which you requested healing and transformation.

Breathe out the negative field, which is negative information, energy, and matter, from the area of your request as you chant *Da Ai*.

Continue this practice for about twenty minutes.

Breathe in.

Breathe out ...

How do you feel?

Here are some results that participants in my live gathering reported after these twenty minutes of practice:

Renewed energy, clarity, and resolve

I am an acupuncturist in the beautiful Pacific Northwest coast in Oregon, USA, and operate a clinic that services people with chronic pain and other health conditions. I am married to my wonderful partner, Dan. My hobbies include spending time with loved ones, going for walks and hikes in nature, and doing volunteer work such as serving the homeless. I love reading, crafts, cooking, and swimming.

When I came across Master Sha's soul over matter techniques in 2015, I was blown away. I immediately started integrating them in my clinic and sharing them with some of my clients. I noticed that those clients responded much faster to the treatments I was giving them and I fell in love with this body of work.

I have been able to heal many areas of my life I never knew were possible because of the work Master Sha has so openly shared. I am a well-trained acupuncturist and expert diagnostician. I have trained with many different doctors and schools of thought when it comes to acupuncture and Chinese medicine. However, nothing could prepare me for how much more effective acupuncture is when combined with Master Sha's techniques.

Master Sha recently offered a group remote healing blessing with a Da Ai *(Greatest Love) Tao Calligraphy he had just written. Prior to this, I had been feeling exhausted with some mental heaviness. After the blessing, I felt a great deal of release and lightness. The symptoms I was experiencing have dissolved and I feel renewed. This Da Ai healing blessing helped me completely turn things around and renewed my state of energy, clarity, and resolve.*

I cannot express my gratitude enough for what I experienced with Tao Calligraphy Transformative Art. It is incredible that this transformed so quickly in a matter of minutes! Thank you from the bottom of my heart for this miracle healing.

— James Carter

Mind-blowing power for healing and transformation

I am married with no children, a retired multi-national business executive, now transformed to a meditation teacher, spiritual healer, and published author.

Today I joined a Tao Calligraphy Transformative Art healing event with Master Sha, who wrote a beyond-powerful Da Ai Tao Calligraphy. My eyes were very tired as it was the end of the day for me. I had a severe headache; the pain was 8–9 out of 10. I was in very deep pain, literally twisting and turning to shake off the pain. I closed my eyes and stayed in the high-frequency field of light as Master Sha offered a xi qing hu zhuo (breathing in the positive Tao Calligraphy Da Ai Field, breathing out the negative field of my headache) self-healing practice with the Da Ai Tao Calligraphy.

After the healing session, my painful headache was totally gone! The speed and power of healing and transformation Tao Calligraphy Transformative Art brings are mind-blowing!

Thank you, Master Sha, for your generosity. I am so grateful for Tao Calligraphy Transformative Art.

— E. O.

Very deep clearing transforms fear

I lived in various beach cities of Los Angeles County for many years, in San Francisco, California for five years, and then in Princeton, New Jersey. Since 2006, I have lived in Bucks County, Pennsylvania, north of Philadelphia along the Delaware River.

Lots of historic farms, stone houses, open space, and multi-family developments growing.

I've had a few different careers, including event planning and designing for trade shows and smaller events, two business partnerships, and selling and marketing of senior living communities. I am an ordained Interfaith Minister and recently certified as an end-of-life doula.

I have been on a spiritual path since I was a young child, greatly influenced by my grandmother. I practiced various meditations, EFT (Emotional Freedom Technique) with great success for several months before my divorce, and spiritual practices, including four years of deep forgiveness practices before hearing of Master Sha.

Words cannot express the peace and nourishment I received when Master Sha offered a healing blessing with the Da Ai Tao Calligraphy he had just written during an online healing event. I requested a healing blessing to transform the unbalanced emotion of fear because I have had much fear arise related to my finances.

During the meditation and breathing practice in the Da Ai Tao Calligraphy Transformative Art Field, I felt gentle radiating heat in my kidneys and up my spine to the base of my neck. I saw faint images with my spiritual channels, including lots of crystal light, and felt tiny vibrations all over my body.

After the healing session, I looked at my bank account balance and my heart was calm. No flutters in my heart or stomach like

I had been experiencing, so I know this was a very deep clearing of blockages for me. I am so grateful.

— Judy Sato

Revolutionary high-frequency healing for humanity

I am a fifty-five-year-old social media expert, consultant, trainer, speaker, and business owner. I live in Gaaden, Austria, a small town close to Vienna, with three cats named San San, Seeker Rose, and Gracie Sophie. Gracie belongs to Andrea, a good friend who lives with me. We live in the quiet countryside at the border of a national park with a forest and a lake nearby. We enjoy nature and love to exercise by walking and running in the woods after work to relax.

About four months ago, I developed liver and gallbladder issues, which started with gallbladder meridian pain that radiated to my back and all the way to the right side of my leg. My liver also became very sensitive to touch.

Due to my daily liver pain (which was typically 6–8 on a scale of 1–10), I had constant tension in my body. Moving my body was uncomfortable and the cool winter air would increase my pain when I went outside. I had pain in my lower back and down my right leg to the knee, which prevented me from exercising. While I normally enjoy walking and running, my movement was limited and I gained weight from lack of exercise. At night I could not sleep on my right side as it caused pain in my very sensitive liver. I was getting impatient and a bit frustrated with my condition. I tried to reduce the pain by changing my eating habits, but it had no effect.

I am so grateful that I had the opportunity to receive a Da Ai Tao Calligraphy Transformative Art healing blessing from Master Sha in a recent event. We did "xi qing hu zhuo" breathing-in and breathing-out practice using the field power of the Da Ai Tao Calligraphy, which Master Sha had just written. Within one hour, my pain was reduced to zero! This is incredibly powerful transformation within such a short period of time. I am so happy that I can move freely and exercise again without pain.

I cannot thank you enough, Master Sha, for bringing this revolutionary high-frequency healing to humanity.

— Natascha Ljubic

I led this practice with the Tao Calligraphy *Da Ai* Field two more times online over the next two days. After completing all three days of practice, here are some additional reports we have received.

My heart melted into absolute peace

I live in Oregon with my husband and worked in the maintenance department of a large manufacturing company. I am now retired.

I was struggling with issues causing negative emotions when Master Sha offered a blessing with his Da Ai *Tao Calligraphy Transformative Art Field during a special event last week. I asked for healing of my emotional heart and felt my heart melt into a state of absolute peace.*

Whatever upset me to begin with is no longer relevant. I am so grateful for this healing through Tao Calligraphy Transformative Art.

— Patricia LeClair

Unexpected benefits

I am a sixty-five-year-old male retired IT Analyst living in the San Francisco Bay Area of California. I am single with one adult daughter. I am fascinated by nature, the fine arts, and personal cultivation. I have studied many ancient traditions and am delighted to share their wisdom and practices with others. My favorite places are Mt. Shasta, Hawaii, Sedona, and Big Sur. I thrive in wild places. At the summer solstice in 2021, I held a spiritual retreat on and around Mt. Shasta.

On January 13, 2022, I received a healing blessing from Master Sha's Da Ai Tao Calligraphy that he wrote during a live webcast event. I became generally more relaxed. My thoughts calmed. I became sleepy.

What I did not expect was the relaxation and greater harmony that I experienced in my neck and jaw. I felt a hush, a silence in my body. While this may seem ordinary for many people, it has been rare for me. I am grateful to have had the opportunity to receive this wonderful blessing from the Tao Source healing field.

— Jeffrey Remis

Wonderful result for dry, painful eyes

I am sixty-six years old and live in a small town in the southwest of Germany. I have worked different jobs, mostly looking at a computer screen for many hours per day. I am divorced with no children and have three sisters and one brother.

I have very dry and painful eyes, which makes work and daily life uncomfortable, stressful, and often very difficult. Sometimes my eyes are extremely tired and I cannot read anything. My eye issue is a result of heavy medications that I took two years ago.

In an introductory Tao Calligraphy Transformative Art event several days ago, Master Sha created a new Tao Calligraphy Da Ai *and generously offered a healing blessing to all participants for one issue of our choosing. He guided us through some breathing practice with the Tao Calligraphy Transformative Art Field. I requested healing for my eyes because they were very dry and painful from too much computer work.*

During the healing and breathing practice, I felt soothing liquid and light coming into my eyes and they relaxed for the first time in weeks. It felt so good. After the event, I felt energy moving not only in my eyes but in my whole body. The next morning, I woke up fresh and could still feel the improvement of my eyes.

It is now nearly a week later and my eyes are tired, but not nearly as much as before the Da Ai healing blessing. They are also not nearly as dry as they were. This is a wonderful result for which I am very grateful.

I will continue to practice and participate in more Tao Calligraphy Transformative Art healing events.

Thank you.

— I. L.

The Tao Calligraphy *Da Ai* Field could transform every aspect of life beyond comprehension. Please start to use the Tao Calligraphy *Da Ai* Field in figure 7. There is no time limit. Da Ai is the greatest healer for all kinds of sickness, including sickness in the physical body, emotional body, mental body, and spiritual body. Da Ai can transform all kinds of relationships. Da Ai can transform your finances and business. Da Ai can open your heart and soul.

As you have read, I led hundreds of people online in three days of the xi qing hu zhuo breathing practice in the Tao Calligraphy *Da Ai* Field for about twenty minutes each day. This field is given to you and humanity in figure 7. I wish you to practice and receive great benefits, and then share this sacred practice with your loved ones.

For Da Ai, the first of the Ten Da greatest qualities, I close with one sentence:

Da Ai, Greatest Love, which is unconditional love, melts all blockages in every aspect of life.

Da Kuan Shu—Greatest Forgiveness:
Brings Inner Joy and Inner Peace

About six years ago, one evening when I was in Los Angeles to teach and heal, I received the Source sacred phrases for Shi Da, which means *Ten Greatest*.

The sacred phrases I received for Da Kuan Shu, Greatest Forgiveness, are:

er da kuan shu   二大宽恕
wo yuan liang ni   我原谅你
ni yuan liang wo   你原谅我
xiang ai ping an he xie   相愛平安和谐

二大宽恕 er da kuan shu
The second of the Ten Da is greatest forgiveness
Er means *second*. Da means *greatest*. Kuan shu means *forgiveness*.

我原谅你 wo yuan liang ni
I forgive you
Wo means *I*. Yuan liang means *to forgive*. Ni means *you*.

你原谅我 ni yuan liang wo
You forgive me

相愛平安和谐 xiang ai ping an he xie
Love, peace, harmony
Xiang ai means *love*. Ping an means *peace*. He xie means *harmony*.

Greatest forgiveness is unconditional forgiveness. Forgiveness is one of the highest secrets for healing. People may not realize that many sicknesses and many relationship and financial challenges are due to anger, depression, anxiety, worry, grief, fear, and other emotional and mental imbalances in one's relationships. *Forgiveness brings inner joy and inner peace.* To forgive others is to balance our emotions and bring peace to our minds. Therefore, forgiveness is one of the golden keys for healing.

Think about your family or your workplace. There may be some relationship challenges among your family members or your coworkers. You may have some relationship challenges yourself with a family member or a coworker. If family members and colleagues could truly offer unconditional forgiveness to each other, their relationship challenges with each other could be resolved quickly.

The four sacred phrases for Da Kuan Shu, Greatest Forgiveness, tell us:

er da kuan shu	*Second is greatest forgiveness*
wo yuan liang ni	*I forgive you*
ni yuan liang wo	*You forgive me*
xiang ai ping an he xie	*Love, peace, harmony*

Whenever you are upset with others or others are upset with you, if you follow these sacred phrases—*I forgive you. You forgive me. Bring love, peace, and harmony*—the upset will be gone. Unfortunately, many people cannot forgive each other. They choose to argue or fight back. There are all kinds of ways to respond negatively. I would like to share more of Lao Zi's great wisdom. In the final chapter of *Dao De Jing*, chapter eighty-one, Lao Zi teaches: "Tian zhi dao, li er bu hai; ren zhi dao, wei er bu zheng." This means *Heaven's nature and rule are to benefit and not harm others; a human's way and rule are to benefit and not fight with others.*

Suppose family member "A" and family member "B" have challenges with each other. If they continue to fight or argue, the challenges will never be resolved. They could get worse and worse. But if "A" sincerely apologizes to "B" and "B" sincerely apologizes to "A" and they forgive each other, then their relationship could quickly transform to one of love, peace, and harmony.

Millions of people believe in Jesus. When Jesus said, "You are forgiven," he was representing the Divine to forgive a person's mistakes. Then miraculous healings of blind people, lepers, paralyzed people, and more, including some distant or remote healings, happened.

What did Jesus do? He sent positive information through the message, "You are forgiven." This positive information carries Divine and Heaven's love, forgiveness, and light. It instantly transformed the person's negative information, energy, and matter, creating a miracle.

The Tao Calligraphy Field also carries positive information, energy, and matter, which could transform negative information, energy, and matter for health, relationships, finances, the spiritual journey, and every aspect of life.

To summarize in one sentence:

Da Kuan Shu, Greatest Forgiveness,
which is unconditional forgiveness, brings
love, peace, and harmony to every aspect of life.

Practice greatest forgiveness. The results could be unbelievable.

Da Ci Bei—Greatest Compassion:
Boosts Energy, Stamina, Vitality,
and Immunity, and Rejuvenates

The third Ten Da greatest quality is Da Ci Bei, Greatest Compassion. The sacred phrases I received from the Source for greatest compassion are:

san da ci bei	三大慈悲
yuan li zeng qiang	愿力增强
fu wu zhong sheng	服务众生
gong de wu liang	功德无量

三大慈悲 san da ci bei
The third greatest quality is greatest compassion
San means *third*. Da means *greatest*. Ci bei means *compassion*.

愿力增强 yuan li zeng qiang
Increase and uplift will power
Yuan li means *will power*. Zeng means *to increase*. Qiang means *strong*.

服务众生 fu wu zhong sheng

Serve humanity
Fu wu means *to serve*. Zhong sheng means *humanity*.

功德无量 gong de wu liang
Virtue is immeasurable
Gong de means *virtue*. Wu liang means *immeasurable*.

In the spiritual journey, if one gives love, care, and help to others unconditionally, Heaven records this service. Heaven then gives Heaven's flowers to this one as a reward. Heaven's flowers are named virtue. Virtue (*gong de* in Chinese) can bless every aspect of life, including for healing, harmonious relationships, flourishing finances, and enlightening the spiritual journey.

san da ci bei	*Third is greatest compassion*
yuan li zeng qiang	*Increases and uplifts will power*
fu wu zhong sheng	*Serve humanity*
gong de wu liang	*Virtue is immeasurable*

Compassion is a very important quality for any human being. Millions of people know Guan Yin, the compassion buddha. She is a universal mother known around the world. Like Jesus, she has saved countless lives miraculously. For example, in ancient times, fishermen out on the ocean would find the weather suddenly change. Huge winds howled and tidal waves capsized the fishermen's boat, throwing them into the ocean. One fisherman was sure he would drown and die, but he remembered to call Heaven: "Guan Yin, jiu ming 观音救命." Jiu means *to save*. Ming means *life*. Guan Yin jiu ming means *Guan Yin, save my life*. After making this desperate appeal, the fisherman sank into the ocean and lost consciousness. When he awoke, he was lying on the seashore. His life was saved. There are many stories like this. Therefore, in Southern China, many large statues of Guan Yin have been constructed, and many temples have been built in China and around the world to honor and commemorate Guan Yin's greatest compassion as a universal mother.

Other stories of Guan Yin's miraculous powers come from people who had stage four metastasized cancer. Medically, they had no hope. But they had reverence for and belief in Guan Yin. They chanted *Na Mo Guan Shi Yin Pusa* 南无观世音菩萨 nonstop. Na mo means *to honor*. Guan Shi Yin, Guan Yin's full name, means *she who hears the cries of humanity's suffering*. Pusa means *bodhisattva*. Many stories have been reported throughout history that these cancer sufferers and others with hopeless conditions were healed.

Guan Yin became a buddha, which is the highest awareness and enlightenment, long long ago. This is the highest achievement on one's spiritual journey. Guan Yin made the biggest vow: "If there is one sentient being who is not enlightened, I will not use the title 'buddha.'" A pusa, or bodhisattva, has reached a very high level of spiritual attainment, just below the buddha level, which is like the highest saint in other traditions. A pusa has not reached complete, highest awareness and enlightenment, but a pusa is still a high-level saint. Guan Yin calls herself a pusa because of her great humility and her biggest vow.

Today Guan Yin is a household name. Not only Buddhists, but literally millions of people around the world of many different belief systems and traditions honor Guan Yin. People deeply love her and respect her. She is truly an unconditional and selfless servant. She is the Bodhisattva of Compassion who lives in people's hearts and souls forever.

Compassion has unique power to boost energy, stamina, vitality, and immunity. Compassion rejuvenates. Compassion increases willpower. Compassion has greatest love. Compassion serves unconditionally. Therefore, Da Ci Bei, Greatest Compassion, is one of the highest qualities in the Ten Da.

In one sentence:

Da Ci Bei, Greatest Compassion, which is unconditional compassion, boosts energy, stamina, vitality, and immunity, as well as rejuvenates, in every aspect of life.

Da Guang Ming—Greatest Light:
Heals and Transforms All Life

The sacred phrases I received for Da Guang Ming, Greatest Light, are:

si da guang ming	四大光明
wo zai Dao guang zhong	我在道光中
Dao guang zai wo zhong	道光在我中
tong ti tou ming	通体透明

四大光明 si da guang ming
The fourth of the ten greatest qualities is greatest light and transparency
Si means *fourth*. Da means *greatest*. Guang ming means *light and transparency*.

我在道光中 wo zai Dao guang zhong
I am within Tao Source light
Wo means *I*. Zai means *to be at*. Dao guang means *Tao Source light*. Zhong means *within*.

道光在我 Dao guang zai wo zhong
Tao Source light is within me
Dao guang means *Tao Source light*. Zai means *to be at*. Wo means *I*. Zhong means *within*.

通体透明 tong ti tou ming
Whole body is transparent
Tong means *whole*. Ti means *body*. Tou ming means *transparent*.

Everybody understands that when you go into a room at night, you need to turn on a light to be able to see. Scientists have shown that the human body shines all kinds of light. This light may not be visible to physical eyes. But it could be visible to special cameras or other special instruments. It could also be visible to some people who have wide-open spiritual channels.

Da Guang Ming is the greatest light from Tao Source. Tao Source light is invisible but it exists. Da Guang Ming connects with Source light. This light can transform our negative information, energy, and matter. Greatest light carries some of the most-positive information, energy, and matter, which can transform every aspect of life, including health, relationships, and finances, and enlighten one's spiritual journey.

si da guang ming	*Fourth is greatest light*
wo zai Dao guang zhong	*I am within Tao Source light*
Dao guang zai wo zhong	*Tao Source light is within me*
tong ti tou ming	*Whole body is transparent*

Imagine you are within Tao Source light. Tao Source light carries Source information, energy, and matter, which is the purest information, energy, and matter, and which can transform the negative information, energy, and matter in every aspect of life. Chanting and visualizing these four lines together is beyond powerful. The benefits could be remarkable beyond comprehension.

In one sentence:

**Da Guang Ming, Greatest Light,
heals and transforms every aspect of life.**

Da Qian Bei—Greatest Humility:
Prevents and Heals Ego in Order to Grow Persistently

I received the following sacred phrases for Da Qian Bei, Greatest Humility, from the Source:

wu da qian bei	五大谦卑
rou ruo bu zheng	柔弱不争

chi xu jing jin   持续精进
shi qian bei   失谦卑
die wan zhang   跌万丈

五大谦卑 wu da qian bei
The fifth of the ten greatest qualities is greatest humility
Wu means *fifth*. Da means *greatest*. Qian bei means *humility*.

柔弱不争 rou ruo bu zheng
Be soft, gentle, and weak; do not fight, strive, or argue
Rou means *soft and gentle*. Ruo means *weak*. Bu zheng means *not to fight, strive, or argue*.

There is a famous statement: di shui chuan shi 滴水穿石, which means *dripping water can pierce through a rock*. Kong Zi, known as Confucius, the founder of Confucianism, met Lao Zi, the author of *Dao De Jing*. One of Lao Zi's major teachings is rou ruo sheng gang qiang 柔弱胜刚强 (*soft and weak can overcome hard and firm*). Lao Zi opened his mouth to show Kong Zi his tongue and missing teeth and asked, "Who stays longer? The teeth or the tongue?" The tongue is soft but stays much longer than the hard teeth.

持续精进 chi xu jing jin
Continue to forge ahead vigorously in every aspect of life.
Chi xu means *to continue*. Jing jin means *to forge ahead vigorously*.

失谦卑 shi qian bei
Lose humility
Shi means *to lose*. Qian bei means *humility*.

跌萬丈 die wan zhang
Fall infinitely deep

Die means *to fall*. Wan means *ten thousand*, which represents *infinite* or *countless* in Chinese. Zhang is a unit of length, *approximately 3.3 meters*.

Wang Yang Ming was a renowned philosopher and calligrapher in early sixteenth century China. One of his most famous teachings is xin xue 心学, which means *heart study*. He also taught, "Ego is the biggest enemy for life." Da Qian Bei, Greatest Humility, is the key to heal ego and prevent ego from developing. Ego can block every aspect of life, including health, relationships, business, finances, and the spiritual journey. Ego could cause one to make huge mistakes. To transform ego is very important to transform all life.

In chapter nine of *Dao De Jing*, Lao Zi wrote: fu gui er jiao, zi yi qi jiu 富贵而骄, 自遗其咎. *Wealth, rank, and pride will bring one disasters.*

wu da qian bei	*Fifth is greatest humility*
rou ruo bu zheng	*Gentle, soft, and weak; do not fight, strive, or argue*
chi xu jing jin	*Continuously move forward with vigor*
shi qian bei	*Lose humility*
die wan zhang	*Fall infinitely deep*

Tao is Greatest Humility. Tao creates everyone and everything. Tao nourishes everyone and everything. Tao does not take credit for anyone or anything. Tao is beyond powerful. Tao is gentle and soft. Tao is unheard, unseen, unfelt. Tao gives us free will. Tao does not interfere, fight, strive, or argue. If we simply connect with Tao through the Tao Calligraphy Field and ask Tao for a blessing, Tao blesses us unconditionally. Therefore, Tao is Greatest Humility.

In one sentence:

**Da Qian Bei, Greatest Humility,
prevents and heals ego in every aspect of life.**

Da He Xie—Greatest Harmony:
The Secret of Success

I received four sacred phrases for Da He Xie, Greatest Harmony:

liu da he xie	六大和谐
san ren tong xin	三人同心
qi li duan jin	其利断金
cheng gong mi jue	成功秘诀

六大和谐 liu da he xie
The sixth of the ten greatest qualities is greatest harmony
Liu means *sixth*. Da means *greatest*. He xie means *harmony*.

三人同心 san ren tong xin
Three people who join hearts together
San means *three*. Ren means *person*. Tong means *to join together*. Xin means *heart*.

其利断金 qi li duan jin
Their strength is like a sharp sword that can cut through gold

Qi refers to *the three people who join hearts together*. Li means *sharp*. Duan means *cut*. Jin means *gold*.

成功秘诀 cheng gong mi jue
The secret of success
Cheng gong means *success*. Mi jue means *secret*.

Three major philosophies and teachings are at the core of Chinese culture: Taoism, Buddhism, and Confucianism. For example, the theory of traditional Chinese medicine comes from Tao teachings.

He xie, which is harmony, is a key teaching in Taoism, Buddhism, Confucianism, and traditional Chinese medicine. For example, a human being has a liver, heart, spleen, lungs, kidneys, brain, and various other organs. Harmony among all of them is the key for health.

Any family needs harmony. There is an ancient statement: jia he wan shi xing 家和萬事興. Jia means *family*. He means *harmonious*. Wan means *ten thousand,* which represents *countless* or *all*. Shi means *thing*. Xing means *to flourish*. Jia he wan shi xing means *a harmonious family brings flourishing to everything*.

Every business and every organization need harmony. Harmony is the vital secret for health, relationships, and success in every aspect of life.

For example, for a business to have success, two teams are needed: the physical team and a Heaven's team. When there is harmony within the physical team, each department and division has harmony with every other department and division, and all the employees have harmony not only with each other but also with many qualities of the business, such as the strategic vision, implementation plans, controls, marketing, and much more. Harmony is the key.

The secret wisdom for success in a person, a family, an organization, a business, a society, a city, a country, Mother Earth, and countless planets, stars, galaxies, and universes is harmony.

liu da he xie	*Sixth is greatest harmony*
san ren tong xin	*Three people who join hearts together*
qi li duan jin	*Their sharpness can cut through gold*
cheng gong mi jue	*The profound secret and key to success*

There is an ancient wisdom: tian ren he yi 天人合一. Tian means *the bigger universe, which is Heaven's team*. Ren *is the small universe, which is a human being's team*. He means *to join as*. Yi means *oneness*. Tian ren he yi means *Heaven's team and a human being's team join as one in greatest harmony*. This is the greatest secret for greatest success.

In one sentence:

**Da He Xie, Greatest Harmony,
is the key to success in every aspect of life.**

Da Chang Sheng—Greatest Flourishing:
The Engine for Further Achievement

I received these sacred phrases for Da Chang Sheng, Greatest Flourishing:

qi da chang sheng	七大昌盛
Dao ci ying fu	道赐盈福
xing shan ji de	行善积德
Dao ye chang sheng	道業昌盛

七大昌盛 qi da chang sheng
The seventh of the ten greatest qualities is greatest flourishing
Qi means *seventh*. Da means *greatest*. Chang sheng means *flourishing* or *prosperous*.

道赐盈福 Dao ci ying fu
Tao Source bestows huge blessings and good fortune in any aspect of life
Dao is Tao Source. Ci means *to bestow*. Ying Fu means *huge blessings and good fortune in any aspect of life*.

行善积德 xing shan ji de
Do kind things to accumulate virtue
Xing means *to act and do*. Shan means *kindness*. Ji means *to accumulate*. De means *virtue*.

道業昌盛 Dao ye chang sheng
Tao career flourishes
Dao is Tao Source. Ye means *career*. Chang sheng means *flourishing* or *prosperous*.

Tao is the Ultimate Creator which creates everyone and everything, including human beings. Tao is within everyone and everything. Every human being has Tao natures and qualities. Human beings' spiritual pollution, including greed; anger; lack of wisdom in activities, actions, behaviors, speech, and thoughts; doubt; ego; and more, blocks our health, relationships, finances, and spiritual journey. For flourishing in every aspect of life, everyone needs to communicate with Tao.

You may not think you know how to communicate with Tao. Tao is The Way of all life. When you follow Tao principles in any aspect of life, including sleeping, eating, raising children, studying, working, conducting business, and more, you *are* communicating with Tao. Then, Tao can bestow huge wisdom and success in every aspect of life.

Tao creates and nourishes everyone and everything. If you serve unconditionally, you will receive much more than someone who does not serve unconditionally. Only through unconditional service can your career be very flourishing. If you serve others, you are following Tao principles. Therefore, your career is a Tao career. If you serve others selfishly, your career is not a Tao career.

The more you apply Ten Da in your occupation or profession, the more your work could flourish. The more you apply Ten Da in your daily life, the more every aspect of your life could flourish.

qi da chang sheng	*Seventh is greatest flourishing*
Dao ci ying fu	*Tao Source bestows huge blessing and fortune*
xing shan ji de	*Do kind things to accumulate virtue*
Dao ye chang sheng	*Tao career flourishes*

Tao creates Heaven, Mother Earth, and countless planets, stars, galaxies, and universes, including human beings. Tao and de nourish everyone and everything. Tao ci ying fu means *Tao bestows huge blessing and fortune in every aspect of life*. These four sacred phrases for Da Chang Sheng teach the secret that if everyone truly connects with Tao, Tao could bestow huge blessing and fortune.

In one sentence:

Da Chang Sheng, Greatest Flourishing, is the energy and support to serve more in every aspect of life.

Da Gan En—Greatest Gratitude:
The Key for Progress

I received these sacred phrases for Da Gan En, Greatest Gratitude:

ba da gan en	八大感恩
Dao sheng de yang	道生德养
zai pei ci hui	栽培赐慧
Dao en yong cun	道恩永存

八大感恩 ba da gan en
The eighth of the Ten Da qualities is greatest gratitude

Ba means *eighth*. Da means *greatest*. Gan en means *gratitude*.

道生德养 Dao sheng de yang
Tao Source creates and de nourishes
Sheng means *creates*. De is the *shen kou yi* (actions, activities, behaviors, speech, thoughts) *and virtue of Tao*. Yang means *nourishes*.

栽培赐慧 zai pei ci hui
Tao Source cultivates and bestows wisdom and intelligence to everyone and everything
Zai pei means *to cultivate, grow, and educate*. Ci means *to bestow*. Hui means *wisdom*.

道恩永存 Dao en yong cun
Our honor of Tao will last forever
En means *honor*. Yong cun means *to exist forever*.

Greatest gratitude is one of the highest qualities we could have. Think about our parents who raised us. Think about our teachers in school—elementary school, high school, and college. Think about our teachers in our occupation or profession. Think about everyone who has nurtured our wisdom, knowledge, love, compassion, and more. Think of those who have been examples for us of how to act and speak. Think of those who corrected our mistakes. Without all of them, we would not have been able to grow into who we are. We need to have gratitude to everyone who has helped us in our life. We also need to have gratitude for the lessons we have learned in life. The lessons we learn make us wiser so that we will not make the same mistakes again.

ba da gan en	*Eighth is greatest gratitude*
Dao sheng de yang	*Tao creates, de nourishes*
zai pei ci hui	*Tao bestows wisdom to all*
Dao en yong cun	*Our honor of Tao will remain forever*

Anyone who holds the greatest gratitude will progress in every aspect of life. Gratitude should come from the heart and soul. Gratitude is so important for life.

Tao Source creates us, nourishes us, and bestows wisdom and grace to us to empower us to succeed in every aspect of life. We cannot express enough the greatest gratitude to Tao and de. Therefore, our honor for the favor, blessings, and grace of Tao and de should always remain in our hearts and souls.

In one sentence:

Da Gan En, Greatest Gratitude, is the key for accelerating success in every aspect of life.

Da Fu Wu—Greatest Service:
The Purpose of Life

The sacred phrases I received for Da Fu Wu, Greatest Service, are:

jiu da fu wu	九大服务
shi wei gong pu	誓为公仆
wu si feng xian	无私奉献
shang cheng fa men	上乘法门

九大服务 jiu da fu wu
The ninth of the Ten Da is greatest service
Jiu means *ninth*. Da means *greatest*. Fu wu means *service*.

誓为公仆 shi wei gong pu
Vow to be a servant of humanity
Shi means *to vow*. Wei means *to be*. Gong pu means *servant of humanity*.

无私奉献 wu si feng xian
Selflessly dedicate yourself to serve others
Wu means *not*. Si means *self*. Feng xian means *to offer to others dedicatedly and devotedly*.

上乘法门 shang cheng fa men
The highest method and gate to healing, transformation, and enlightenment of one's soul, heart, mind, and body
Shang cheng means *highest*. Fa means *dharma*. Men means *gate* or *door*.

The purpose of life is to serve. I have committed my life to this purpose. To serve is to make others happier and healthier. To serve is to empower and enlighten others.

A human being has a physical life and a spiritual journey. The physical life is limited. The spiritual journey is eternal. Physical life is given to us so that we can serve our spiritual journey, which is our soul's life.

There are two kinds of services and benefits. One kind is to serve yourself to achieve your own success and enlightenment. The other kind is to serve others to help make others successful and enlightened. Many people think to serve oneself is the priority. In fact, to serve, empower, and enlighten others is much more important.

Why does a person suffer? High-level spiritual wisdom explains that a person suffers due to self-attachment or self-centeredness. A person could turn everything they think about into thinking about themselves. This could manifest as greed; anger; lack of wisdom in what they do, what they speak, and what they think; doubt; ego; competition; jealousy, a fighting nature; and more. I have explained these earlier. I emphasize again: These qualities of self-attachment and self-centeredness are all spiritual pollution in the heart and soul. These natures of self-attachment are the root cause of all challenges in health, relationships, finances, and the spiritual journey.

To transform health, relationships, finances, and the spiritual journey, the key is less "me, me, me," less self-centeredness, and less self-attachment. A highly-enlightened spiritual being could reach the condition of completely removing "me, me, me." If one can serve others unconditionally and selflessly, every aspect of life could be transformed beyond words. I am delighted to share a one-sentence secret:

To serve others is to reduce "me, me, me"; to serve others unconditionally is to reach no "me, me, me."

Guan Yin, the Compassion Buddha, served humanity and all souls unconditionally for millions of lifetimes. Therefore, she has become a universal mother. Heaven and Tao gave her the honorable title of Qian Shou Qian Yan (*Thousand Hands, Thousand Eyes*) Da Ci Da Bei (*Greatest Compassion*) Jiu Ku Jiu Nan (*Saving Humans from Bitterness and Disasters*) Guang Da Yuan Man (*Greatest Enlightenment*) Buddha.

If you commit to serve others unconditionally, others may not become enlightened, but you could become enlightened first.

To enlighten your soul, serving unconditionally is a *must*. What does it mean to serve unconditionally? To serve unconditionally is to serve without "me, me, me." One needs to serve selflessly, without "me, me, me."

Shen kou yi is our daily life. Shen means *activities, actions, and behaviors*. Kou means *speech*. Yi means *thoughts*. Every day, everyone has shen kou yi. Can we focus our shen kou yi on serving others unconditionally? Selflessly? If so, you could receive remarkable transformation in your health, relationships, and finances, and receive unimaginable upliftment for your soul enlightenment journey.

jiu da fu wu	*Ninth of the Ten Da qualities is Greatest Service*
shi wei gong pu	*Vow to serve humanity*
wu si feng xian	*Selflessly devote yourself to serve others*
shang cheng fa men	*The highest method and gate to enlightenment*

There is a universal law called the Universal Law of Universal Service. It begins with these three statements:

Serve others a little,
receive a little reward from Tao Source.

Serve others more,
receive more reward from Tao Source.

Serve others unconditionally,
receive unlimited reward from Tao Source.

It does not matter who you are. It does not matter what job you are doing. In what you do, in what you speak, and in what you think, always remember to make others healthier, happier, empowered, and enlightened.

Humanity has all kinds of challenges, including in health, relationships, finances, and the spiritual journey. The absolute key for service is selfless service or unconditional service to others, without "me, me, me." It is easy to say but very difficult to do.

Therefore, Da Fu Wu, greatest, unconditional, and selfless service, carries Tao information, energy, and matter, which can transform our negative information, energy, and matter so that we can serve others unconditionally and selflessly.

In one sentence:

Da Fu Wu, Greatest Service,
is the purpose of life in every aspect.

Da Yuan Man—Greatest Enlightenment:
The Ultimate Achievement for One's Life

Tao Source gave me four sacred phrases for Da Yuan Man, Greatest Enlightenment:

shi da yuan man	十大圆满
ling xin nao shen yuan man	靈心脑身圆满
ren di tian Dao shen xian ti	人地天道神仙梯
fu wu xiu lian cai ke pan	服务修炼才可攀

十大圆满 shi da yuan man
The tenth of the Ten Da qualities is Greatest Enlightenment
Shi means *tenth*. Da means *greatest*. Yuan man means *enlightenment*.

靈心脑身圆满 ling xin nao shen yuan man
Soul, heart, mind, and body enlightenment
Ling means *soul*. Xin means *heart*, which is the core of life. (This is the spiritual heart, which is the receiver of the information or messages from the soul. A human has a heart. A pet has a heart. Does a mountain have a heart? Does an ocean have a heart? Does Mother Earth have a heart? The answers are "yes." Living things have hearts. Inanimate things also have hearts.) Nao means *consciousness*. Shen means *body*. For the enlightenment journey, enlighten the soul first. Then, enlighten the heart. Next, enlighten the mind. Finally, enlighten the body.

人地天道神仙梯 ren di tian Dao shen xian ti
Saints have four major levels or steps: human saint, Mother Earth saint, Heaven saint, and Tao saint

Ren means *human being*. Di means *Mother Earth*. Tian means *Heaven*.

Dao is Tao Source. Shen xian means *saints*. Ti means *stairs*.

What is a saint? A saint has reached awareness. Awareness means to realize the universal truths and to embody the universal truths. Ten Da is the highest universal truth. Ten Da is Tao Source nature. Awareness has layers. Therefore, there are four major layers of saints.

Ren xian 人仙 means *human saint*. A ren xian can transform a human being's conditions. Human saints have also reached the fan lao huan tong 返老还童 condition. Fan means *to return*. Lao means *old age*. Huan also means *to return* or *to go back to*. Tong means *the baby state*. Fan lao huan tong means *return from old age to the purity and health of the baby state*. It is true rejuvenation.

Di xian 地仙 means *Mother Earth saint*. The quality of a di xian is very high. A di xian can transform Mother Earth's conditions.

Tian xian 天仙 means *Heaven saint*. A tian xian has even higher abilities that can transform Heaven's conditions.

Dao xian 道仙 is a *Tao Source saint*, the highest saint. A Dao xian can transform countless planets, stars, galaxies, and universes, because Tao is the Ultimate Creator and Source of countless planets, stars, galaxies, and universes.

The wisdom of the four layers of saints (ren xian, di xian, tian xian, Dao xian) is ancient secret Tao wisdom. What are the power and significance of being a ren xian, di xian, tian xian, or Dao xian? How do the saints climb the stairs to reach higher and higher layers? I have shared more profound ancient wisdom and secret practices in three books I have written on Tao.[4] If you are inspired to learn more about this advanced soul achievement, please read and practice with them.

服务修炼才可攀 fu wu xiu lian cai ke pan

Serving unconditionally is the only way to climb Heaven's and Tao's stairs to become a ren xian, di xian, tian xian, and Dao xian

Fu wu means *service*. Xiu means *purification*. Lian means *practice*. Xiu lian means *purification practice*. Fu wu xiu lian is *service purification practice*, which is to serve unconditionally. There are many spiritual belief systems. Each spiritual belief system teaches and does xiu lian in their own way. The essence is the same. Cai means *only*. Ke means *to be able*. Pan means *to climb*.

Xiu lian can be explained in one sentence:

Xiu lian is to purify a human's shen kou yi, including activities, actions, behaviors, speech, and thoughts, to a saint's shen kou yi.

[4] Zhi Gang Sha, *Tao I: The Way of All Life* (New York, New York/Toronto, Ontario: Atria Books/Heaven's Library Pub. Corp., 2010); *Tao II: The Way of Healing, Rejuvenation, Longevity, and Immortality* (New York, New York/Toronto, Ontario: Atria Books/Heaven's Library Pub. Corp., 2010); *Tao Classic of Longevity and Immortality: Sacred Wisdom and Practical Techniques* (Dallas, Texas/Richmond Hill, Ontario: BenBella Books/Heaven's Library Pub. Corp., 2018).

What is a human's shen kou yi? Human shen kou yi comes from self-attachment and self-centeredness. In every aspect of life, this is to consider "me, me, me" first. The purpose of xiu lian is to purify selfishness to selfless-ness. I cannot emphasize enough that to truly purify is to remove all kinds of human pollution, including:

- tan 贪 *greed*
- chen 嗔 *anger*
- chi 痴 *lack of wisdom in shen kou yi*
- yi 疑 *doubt*
- man 慢 *ego*
- ming 名 *fame*
- li 利 *focus on money and power*
- zheng dou 争斗 *fighting*
- du ji 妒忌 *jealousy*
- jing zheng 竞争 *competition*
- and more

Remove the above human pollution in order to reach a saint's level. Purify further and serve unconditionally to reach higher and higher layers of enlightenment.

shi da yuan man	*The tenth of the Ten Da qualities is Greatest Enlightenment*
ling xin nao shen yuan man	*Soul, heart, mind, and body enlightenment*

ren di tian Dao shen xian ti	*Saints have four major levels or steps: human saint, Mother Earth saint, Heaven saint, and Tao saint*
fu wu xiu lian cai ke pan	*Unconditional service is the only way to climb Heaven's and Tao's stairs*

In one sentence:

**Da Yuan Man, Greatest Enlightenment,
is the ultimate goal and achievement of
one's spiritual journey and physical journey.**

ಔ ಠಿ ಞ

Shi Da, the ten greatest qualities, is Tao Source nature, as well as Source wisdom and power to transform every aspect of life, including health, relationships, finances, and the spiritual journey.

Tao Calligraphy carries a Source field, which includes Source love and light; Source frequency and vibration; Source most-positive information, energy, and matter; Source unlimited capabilities; and Source highest power of soul over matter, which could transform negative information, energy, and matter in every aspect of life.

In the next chapter I will guide you to apply the Tao Calligraphy *Da Ai* Field to transform every aspect of life.

Tao Calligraphy
Field Transformation

I WOULD LIKE to emphasize again that Tao:

- is the Ultimate Creator and Source

- carries Source love and light

- carries Source frequency and vibration

- carries Source most-positive information, energy, and matter that could transform every aspect of life, including health, relationships, finances, and the spiritual journey

- carries Source infinite abilities

- is the highest soul that carries the highest power of soul over matter. Soul over matter is soulfulness, which means soul can make things happen. Because Tao is the Ultimate Creator and Source, it has the highest soul power to transform every aspect of life.

Calligraphy is art.

Tao Calligraphy is Source Oneness art that creates and carries a Tao Source Field as a physical presence of Tao on Mother Earth. In chapter eleven, Dr. Peter Hudoba will share some key findings of medical research he has conducted on the Tao Calligraphy Transformative Art Field to help you understand clearly the effectiveness of the Tao Calligraphy Field for transforming health conditions.

Tao Calligraphy *Da Ai* Field

In the previous chapter, I shared the Tao Calligraphy *Da Ai* Field I created in figure 7. I asked you to practice with this field for twenty minutes to serve one request. In this chapter, I will guide you to apply the Tao Calligraphy *Da Ai* Field to transform health, relationships, finances, and the spiritual journey.

Tao Calligraphy *Da Ai* Field
Transforms Health for the Physical Body

Let us apply the Six Power Techniques.

Body Power

Body Power is to use body and hand positions for healing.

Sit up straight with your back free and clear and your feet flat on the floor. Put one palm over your navel and the other palm over any part of your body where you wish to receive healing, transformation, prevention, or rejuvenation.

Soul Power

Soul Power is to apply soul over matter or soulfulness by invoking inner souls within our body and outer souls outside our body. I gave Soul Power the name "Say Hello Healing and Transformation" more than fifteen years ago.

"Say hello" to inner souls:

> *Dear soul, heart, mind, and body (or shen qi jing) of my*
> _____ (name the system, organ, part or area of the body, or physical health condition for which you wish healing[5]),
> *I love you, honor you, and appreciate you.*
> *You have the power to heal yourself.*
> *Do a great job.*
> *Thank you.*

"Say hello" to outer souls:

> *Dear the Tao Calligraphy* Da Ai *Field,*
> *Dear Tao Source,*
> *Dear Divine,*
> *Dear all my spiritual fathers and mothers, angels, guides, and protectors,*
> *I love you, honor you, and appreciate you.*
> *Please give me a healing for my* _____ (repeat your request).

---

[5] Some examples: my heart, my respiratory system, my knees, my lower back, my hypertension, my breast cancer, my migraines, etc. Any physical system, organ, part or area of the body, pain, cyst, tumor, sickness, or physical condition is fine.

I am very grateful.
Thank you.

If you want to request prevention of sickness or rejuvenation, simply replace (or add) those words for "healing."

Breathing Power, Mind Power, Sound Power, and Tao Calligraphy Field Power

Breathing Power, Mind Power, Sound Power, and Tao Calligraphy Field Power are the remaining four of the Six Power Techniques.

For Breathing Power, we will use the ancient secret breathing practice named xi qing hu zhuo 吸清呼浊 that I introduced in the previous chapter (page 72). Remember that xi qing means *inhale positive shen qi jing* and hu zhuo means *exhale negative shen qi jing*. We all know life is breathing in and breathing out. Breathe in oxygen and breathe out carbon dioxide.

We combine the Xi Qing Hu Zhuo Breathing Power technique with Tao Calligraphy Field Power. This breakthrough synergy is much more powerful than the ancient breathing practice alone because the Tao Calligraphy Field is a Source most-positive shen qi jing field (information energy matter field).

Xi qing is to breathe in the positive information, energy, and matter of the *Da Ai* Tao Calligraphy Field. Have the *Da Ai* Tao Calligraphy Field in figure 7 in front of you as you do the practices in this chapter that use it.

Now, combine Breathing Power and Tao Calligraphy Field Power with Mind Power.

As you inhale deeply and slowly, visualize golden light from the *Da Ai* Tao Calligraphy Field coming to and gathering in the part or area of the physical body for which you requested healing. This golden light carries the most-positive information, energy, and matter of the Tao Calligraphy *Da Ai* Field.

Finally, add Sound Power.

As you exhale, chant *Da Ai* (pronounced *dah eye*) and visualize the golden light radiating in all directions from the area for which you requested healing, filling your whole body as you exhale negative information, energy, and matter from your request.

Continue to practice. It is best to practice for at least ten to twenty minutes per time, and you can practice several times per day. In fact, there is no time limit for this practice. For chronic pain and life-threatening conditions, practice for a total of one to two hours a day. The benefits could be beyond your comprehension.

Tao Calligraphy *Da Ai* Field
Transforms Health for the Emotional Body

Everyone can use healing, transformation, prevention, and rejuvenation for the physical body. Therefore, study the preceding section, practice well, and, most important, do it!

To use the Six Power Techniques to transform the health of the emotional body, which is to reduce, remove, and prevent unbalanced emotions, simply modify the Mind Power used in the previous practice (transforming health for the physical body) as follows:

For anger, visualize the golden light gathering in and around the liver as you inhale and radiating in all directions from your liver as you exhale, releasing negative shen qi jing.

For anxiety or depression, visualize the golden light gathering in and around your heart.

For worry, visualize the golden light gathering in and around your spleen.

For sadness or grief, visualize the golden light gathering in and around your lungs.

For fear, visualize the golden light gathering in and around your kidneys.

For other unbalanced emotions, such as guilt or shame, visualize the golden light gathering in and around your heart.

These guidelines are based on the Five Elements theory of traditional Chinese medicine. I will explain a little more about the Five Elements theory later in this chapter.

Tao Calligraphy *Da Ai* Field Transforms Health for the Mental Body

For the mental body, you may wish healing, transformation, or prevention for issues such as negative attitudes, negative mind-sets, negative beliefs, ego, attachments, or any other mental condition.

Follow the pattern of the practice for the physical body earlier in this chapter. For Mind Power, visualize golden light from the *Da Ai* Tao Calligraphy Field coming to both the heart and the brain together. The heart houses the mind and soul.

Tao Calligraphy *Da Ai* Field Transforms Health for the Spiritual Body

To transform health for the spiritual body is to transform negative information, energy, and matter blocking one's spiritual journey. This could include issues such as lack of belief, lack of trust, doubt, lack of discipline, resistance of all kinds, and more.

Follow the pattern of the practice for the physical body earlier in this chapter. For Mind Power, visualize golden light from the *Da Ai* Tao Calligraphy Field coming to the heart.

In this and the earlier practices, practice at least ten minutes per time, two or three times a day. For chronic or life-threatening conditions, practice for a total of two hours a day. In fact, there is no time limit. I cannot emphasize enough that life is breathing in and breathing out. You can practice for many hours a day, especially if you have a serious or life-threatening condition. Each time you practice, keep the book open to figure 7.

Patience and persistence are important. We have had thousands of heart-touching and moving results worldwide. I wish each of you to receive the greatest benefits you can.

Practice. Practice. Practice.
Heal. Heal. Heal.
Transform. Transform. Transform.
Restore your health as soon as possible.

Tao Calligraphy *Da Ai* Field Transforms Relationships

The Tao Calligraphy Transformative Art Field is a Source Field, which is a quantum field with unlimited positive information, energy, and matter and unlimited potential. That is why the Tao Calligraphy Field can heal and transform any aspect of life, including relationships.

Few people have only perfect relationships full of love, peace, and harmony. Most people could have one or several challenging relationships. Some people have huge challenges in relationships.

Apply the Six Power Techniques to transform negative information, energy, and matter in one or more relationships.

Body Power

Sit up straight with your back free and clear and your feet flat on the floor. You may also stand up straight with your feet shoulder-width apart. Put one palm over your navel and the other palm over your first energy chakra (root chakra) at the bottom of your torso. The first energy chakra is important for relationships. See figure 9 for the location of the first energy chakra.

Soul Power

"Say hello" to inner souls:

Dear soul, heart, mind, and body (or *shen qi jing*) *of my relationship with* _____ (name the person or persons),
I love you, honor you, and appreciate you.
You have the power to heal and transform yourself.
Do a great job.
Thank you.

"Say hello" to outer souls:

Dear _____ (name the person or persons),
I love you, honor you, and appreciate you.
We have some challenges in our relationship.
We have the power to heal and transform our relationship.
I forgive you.
You forgive me.
Bring love, peace, and harmony.

Dear the Tao Calligraphy Da Ai *Field,*
Dear Tao Source,
Dear Divine,
Dear all our (your and the other person's) *spiritual*
    fathers and mothers, angels, guides, and protectors,
I love you, honor you, and appreciate you.
Please give us a blessing to heal and transform my
    relationship with _____ (name the person or
    persons again).
I am very grateful.
Thank you.

Breathing Power, Mind Power, Sound Power, and Tao Calligraphy Field Power

Use the Xi Qing Hu Zhuo (Inhale Positive, Exhale Negative) Breathing Power technique. Open the book to figure 7 and breathe in the positive information, energy, and matter of the *Da Ai* Tao Calligraphy Field. As you inhale, visualize golden light from the *Da Ai* Tao Calligraphy Field coming to and gathering in your first energy chakra.

As you exhale, chant *Da Ai* and visualize the golden light radiating in all directions from your first energy chakra, filling your whole body as you exhale negative information, energy, and matter from your relationship.

Continue to practice for at least ten minutes per time. You can practice several times per day. In fact, there is no time limit for this practice.

Tao Calligraphy *Da Ai* Field
Transforms Finances

Apply the Six Power Techniques to transform negative information, energy, and matter in your finances.

Body Power

Sit up straight with your back free and clear and your feet flat on the floor. You may also stand up straight with your feet shoulder-width apart. Put one palm over your navel and the other palm just below, over your second energy chakra in your lower abdomen. The second energy chakra is important for finances. See figure 9 for the location of the second energy chakra.

Soul Power

"Say hello" to inner souls:

Dear soul, heart, mind, and body (or shen qi jing) of my
  finances,
I love you, honor you, and appreciate you.
You have the power to heal and transform yourself.
Do a great job.
Thank you.

"Say hello" to outer souls:

Dear the Tao Calligraphy Da Ai *Field,*
Dear Tao Source,
Dear Divine,

Dear all my spiritual fathers and mothers, angels, guides,
   and protectors,
I love you, honor you, and appreciate you.
Please give me a blessing to heal and transform my
   finances.
I am very grateful.
Thank you.

Breathing Power, Mind Power, Sound Power, and Tao Calligraphy Field Power

Use the Xi Qing Hu Zhuo (Inhale Positive, Exhale Negative) Breathing Power technique. Open the book to figure 7 and breathe in the positive information, energy, and matter of the *Da Ai* Tao Calligraphy Field. As you inhale, visualize golden light from the *Da Ai* Tao Calligraphy Field coming to and gathering in your second energy chakra.

As you exhale, chant *Da Ai* and visualize the golden light radiating in all directions from your second energy chakra, filling your whole body as you exhale negative information, energy, and matter from your finances.

Continue to practice for at least ten minutes per time. You can practice several times per day. In fact, there is no time limit for this practice.

Zhong Mai Healing and Transformation

There is an ancient secret wisdom and practice to heal and transform the physical, emotional, mental, and spiritual bodies. In fact, this secret wisdom and practice can help heal and transform any aspect of life, including relationships and finances. It is named Zhong Mai Healing and Transformation. Zhong means *central*. Mai means *meridian*.

The Zhong Mai is a vertical channel in the center of the body from the bottom of the torso to the top of the head. It starts at the Hui Yin acupuncture point and ends at the Bai Hui acupuncture point. The Hui Yin acupuncture point is at the bottom of the torso. It lies between the anus and the external genitals on the perineum. The Bai Hui acupuncture point is at the center of the top of the head. Imagine a line running along the center of the top of your head, between the left and right sides. Now imagine a line connecting the tops of your ears running across the top of your head. The Bai Hui acupuncture point is at the intersection of these two lines.

These two acupuncture points (see figure 9) play a major role in balancing yin and yang. The Hui Yin point absorbs Mother Earth's energy. The Bai Hui point absorbs Heaven's energy. Mother Earth is yin. Heaven is yang. For five thousand years in traditional Chinese medicine, the number one principle for healing is to balance yin and yang.

Yang is the nature of fire. Fire is hot, ascending, and exciting. Yin is the nature of water. Water is cool, descending, and calm. Every system, every organ, every cell, and every part of the body are divided into yin and yang. For example, the back of the body is yang; the front of the body is yin. The upper part of the body is yang; the lower part is yin. The outside of the body is yang; the inside is yin.

The internal organs of the body are also categorized between yin and yang according to the Five Elements theory used in traditional Chinese medicine. The major yin-yang organ pairs are:

- Wood element: liver–gallbladder

- Fire element: heart–small intestine

- Earth element: spleen–stomach

- Metal element: lungs–large intestine

- Water element: kidneys–urinary bladder

In figure 8, I share some additional basic wisdom of Five Elements theory for the physical body, emotional body, and more.[6]

The wisdom goes deeper. Every organ is divided into yin and yang. Every cell is also divided into yin and yang. Yin yang balance is healing. Excessive or insufficient yin causes sickness. Excessive or insufficient yang also causes sickness.

The Zhong Mai runs through and connects with seven major energy centers or chakras. In traditional Tao teaching, they are called:

---

[6] For deeper wisdom about Five Elements theory, see my book *Soul Healing Miracles: Ancient and New Sacred Wisdom, Knowledge, and Practical Techniques for Healing the Spiritual, Mental, Emotional, and Physical Bodies* (Dallas, Texas/Toronto, Ontario: BenBella Books/Heaven's Library Publication Corp.,2013).

Element	Yin Organ	Yang Organ	Sense	Body Tissue
Wood	Liver	Gallbladder	Eyes Sight	Tendons Nails
Fire	Heart	Small Intestine	Tongue Taste	Blood Vessels
Earth	Spleen	Stomach	Mouth Lips Speech	Muscles
Metal	Lungs	Large Intestine	Nose Smell	Skin
Water	Kidneys	Urinary Bladder	Ears Hearing	Bones Joints

Element	Unbalanced Emotion	Balanced Emotion	Body Fluid	Finger
Wood	Anger	Patience	Tears	Index
Fire	Depression Anxiety Excitability	Joy	Sweat	Middle
Earth	Worry	Love Compassion	Saliva	Thumb
Metal	Grief Sadness	Courage	Mucus	Ring
Water	Fear	Calmness	Urine	Little

Figure 8. Five Elements

1st energy chakra: 海地轮 Gear at the Bottom of the Ocean

2nd energy chakra: 水轮 Water Gear

3rd energy chakra: 日轮 Sun Gear

4th energy chakra: 火轮 Fire Gear

5th energy chakra: 风轮 Wind Gear

6th energy chakra: 月轮 Moon Gear

7th energy chakra: 天轮 Heaven Gear

These are the central spaces in the body. See figure 9.

Figure 9. Seven Energy Chakras or Gears

The Zhong Mai also goes through San Jiao, which is often called the Triple Burner or Triple Warmer in English. It consists of three major spaces in the body. The Lower Jiao is the space in the torso below the level of the navel. The Middle Jiao is the space between the levels of the navel and the diaphragm. The Upper Jiao is the space above the diaphragm. See figure 10.

Figure 10. San Jiao

In traditional Chinese medicine, San Jiao is the pathway of qi and body fluids.

中脉一通, 百脉通

zhong mai yi tong, bai mai tong

If the central meridian flows freely, all meridians flow freely.

三焦畅通, 百病消除

san jiao chang tong, bai bing xiao chu

If San Jiao flows freely, all sicknesses are removed.

For the central meridian to flow freely, blockages in all seven energy chakras or gears must be removed. Blockages are negative shen qi jing. Each energy chakra connects closely with various aspects of our soul, heart, mind, and body. For example, the third energy chakra or Sun Gear connects with the Wood element, including the liver, gallbladder, eyes, tendons, and anger, and with the Water element, including the kidneys, urinary bladder, ears, bones, joints, and fear, while the sixth energy chakra or Moon Gear is very important for developing mind intelligence.

All seven energy chakras or gears together connect with every aspect of our soul, heart, mind, and body. Therefore, zhong mai yi tong, bai mai tong. This means *if the central meridian flows freely, all meridians flow freely.* It is vital to heal and transform the seven energy chakras and the Zhong Mai for all healing and transformation in our soul, heart, mind, and body.

San jiao chang tong, bai bing xiao chu (*if San Jiao flows freely, all sicknesses are removed*) tells us it is also vital to heal and transform negative shen qi jing in San Jiao for all other healing and transformation.

What is the best way to heal and transform the seven energy chakras, the Zhong Mai, and San Jiao?

Is there a way to heal and transform the seven energy chakras, the Zhong Mai, and San Jiao together?

My answer is *yes*! I am honored to share this secret and sacred way in the next section.

Qi Channel

The Qi Channel is the most important energy channel in the body. The Qi Channel starts from the Hui Yin acupuncture point, goes up the Zhong Mai to the Bai Hui acupuncture point, then turns down through the back of the head and in front of the spinal column, through Wai Jiao, returning to the Hui Yin acupuncture point. See figure 11.

Wai Jiao is the biggest space in the body. It is the space in the back of the head and in front of the entire spinal column. See figure 11. San Jiao and Wai Jiao partially overlap, so they are closely related. Specifically, San Jiao (Lower, Middle, and Upper) is like three rivers, and Wai Jiao is the ocean into which they flow. If San Jiao is blocked, Wai Jiao will be blocked. Therefore, if Wai Jiao is clear, San Jiao will be clear as well. Remember the ancient wisdom: san jiao chang tong, bai bing xiao chu (*if San Jiao flows freely, all sicknesses are removed*).

The Qi Channel connects the seven energy chakras or gears, the Zhong Mai, and Wai Jiao. Therefore, there is a way to heal and transform the seven energy chakras, the

Zhong Mai, and San Jiao together. What is the way? In one sentence:

To heal and transform the Qi Channel is to heal and transform the seven energy chakras, the Zhong Mai, San Jiao, and Wai Jiao together, which supports healing and transformation of the physical body, emotional body, mental body, spiritual body, relationships, finances, and every aspect of life.

Wai Jiao is the shaded space in the back of the head and in front of the spinal column.

Figure 11. Qi Channel and Wai Jiao

What is the way to heal and transform the Qi Channel?

I received secret and sacred mantras from the Source for the seven energy chakras or gears and Wai Jiao. See figure 11.

- The secret mantra for the 1st energy chakra is Hei (pronounced *hay*).

- The secret mantra for the 2nd energy chakra is Heng (pronounced *hung*).

- The secret mantra for the 3rd energy chakra is Hong (pronounced *hōng*).

- The secret mantra for the 4th energy chakra is Ah (pronounced *ah*).

- The secret mantra for the 5th energy chakra is Xi (pronounced *shee*).

- The secret mantra for the 6th energy chakra is Yi (pronounced *ee*).

- The secret mantra for the 7th energy chakra is Weng (pronounced *wung*).

- The secret mantra for Wai Jiao is You (pronounced *yō*).

Therefore, the secret and sacred mantra for the Qi Channel is:

Hei Heng Hong Ah Xi Yi Weng You

For true healing and transformation of any part of the body, chant this mantra three times per day, ten minutes per time. I have created an animation where you can chant with me. You can also apply Mind Power to do the visualizations shown in the animation.

You can view the animation of the practice of the mantra for the Qi Channel through this QR code:

or on this webpage: **https://tchryb.heavenslibrary.com**

For best benefits, remember to apply Soul Power with the Say Hello Healing and Transformation technique, before you begin chanting:

"Say hello" to inner souls:

> *Dear my Qi Channel, seven energy chakras, Zhong Mai,*
> *San Jiao, and Wai Jiao,*
> *I love you.*
> *You have the power to clear and boost yourselves.*
> *Do a great job.*
> *Thank you.*

"Say hello" to outer souls:

> *Dear the animation and secret, sacred mantra for the Qi*
> *Channel,*
> *I love you, honor you, and appreciate you.*

Please clear and boost my Qi Channel and everything
   along its path.
I am very grateful.
Thank you.

Then, chant—with or without the animation—for ten minutes or more.

In fact, there is no time limit for doing the practice shown in the animation. For chronic pain and life-threatening conditions, do the practice for the Qi Channel for one to two hours a day. The benefits could be beyond your comprehension. I have applied this secret wisdom and practice to create many heart-touching and amazing results. I am delighted to release this as one of the highest self-healing secrets for humanity. My message of healing is:

I have the power to heal myself.
You have the power to heal yourself.
Together we have the power to heal the world.

To promote qi flow in the Zhong Mai is to heal the whole body.

To promote qi flow in San Jiao is to heal the whole body.

To promote qi flow in Wai Jiao is to heal the whole body.

To promote qi flow in the Qi Channel, one could get even faster and better results for healing the whole body.

When we are sick, we need doctors. We need healthcare professionals. I support all conventional and alternative and complementary medicines, all healing modalities. I just want you and humanity to realize that the human body has a self-restoring system. We need to activate it. We need to realize we can do amazing healing beyond our comprehension. I wish each reader to understand my message and to do more practice.

Practice. Practice. Practice.
Heal. Heal. Heal.
Transform. Transform. Transform.
Restore your health as quickly as possible.

Heal Your Back with the
Tao Calligraphy Tao Bei Field

YOU COULD RECEIVE benefits from Tao Calligraphy Transformative Art that are beyond comprehension. Tao Calligraphy Transformative Art can help you heal and transform your health, relationships, finances, spiritual journey, and every aspect of life.

In this chapter, I focus on healing and transforming back pain. The majority of humanity will suffer from significant back pain at some point in their lives. In North America, up to seventy to eighty percent of people will experience it at some time.

The transformative art tool is the Tao Calligraphy *Tao Bei* 道背. Tao is the Source. Bei means *back*. The *Tao Bei* Tao Calligraphy Field covers the whole back, from the neck to the tailbone.

The *Tao Bei* Tao Calligraphy for your use is on the back cover.

Let's practice receiving healing, prevention, rejuvenation, and more from the *Tao Bei* Tao Calligraphy Field.

We will use the Xi Qing Hu Zhuo Breathing Power technique that I introduced in chapter eight. This is the key practice technique for healing all sickness. This technique will be used in all future books in my Tao Calligraphy series.

Xi Qing Hu Zhuo (Inhale Positive, Exhale Negative) Practice for the Back

Apply the Six Power Techniques.

Body Power

Put the Tao Calligraphy *Tao Bei* on the back cover over the area of your back where you want healing.

Soul Power

"Say hello" to inner souls:

> *Dear soul, heart, mind, and body* (or *shen qi jing*) *of my back,*
> *I love you, honor you, and appreciate you.*
> *You have the power to heal yourself.*
> *Do a great job.*
> *Thank you.*

"Say hello" to outer souls:

> *Dear the Tao Calligraphy* Tao Bei *Field,*

Dear Tao Source,
Dear Divine,
Dear all my spiritual fathers and mothers, angels, guides,
    and protectors,
I love you, honor you, and appreciate you.
Please give me a healing for my back.
I am very grateful.
Thank you.

Breathing Power, Mind Power, Sound Power, and Tao Calligraphy Field Power

Inhale and visualize golden light from the *Tao Bei* Tao Calligraphy Field on the back cover gathering in the area of the back for which you want healing.

As you exhale, chant *Tao Bei* (pronounced *dao bay*) or *Tao Back* or *Tao Calligraphy Field* and visualize the golden light radiating in all directions as you exhale negative information, energy, and matter from your back.

You can view the animation of the practice with the *Tao Bei* Tao Calligraphy through this QR code:

or on this webpage: **https://tchryb.heavenslibrary.com**

Continue the breathing in, breathing out practice. It is best to practice for at least ten minutes per time, and you can practice several times per day. In fact, there is no time limit for this practice. For chronic pain, practice several times a day so that your total practice time each day is one to two hours. The benefits could be beyond your comprehension.

The *Tao Bei* Tao Calligraphy on the back cover is the one I wrote in January 2022 during a healing session webcast to hundreds of people around the world. I am delighted to share some of the many reports of the participants' experiences as and after we practiced together in the Tao Calligraphy *Tao Bei* Field. Many people experienced the Tao Calligraphy Field even as I was writing this Tao Calligraphy.

I sincerely wish you to use the Tao Calligraphy *Tao Bei* Field more for healing, prevention, rejuvenation, and prolonging the life of your back.

Many people worldwide have already experienced a profound transformation of their back pain (and even of issues apart from the back) from the Tao Calligraphy *Tao Bei* Transformative Art Field. May you be inspired to use the Tao Calligraphy Field more. The Tao Calligraphy Transformative Art Field is available for you here and now.

⫷ ⫷ ⫸

Shocked by my experience with Tao Calligraphy Transformative Art

I live in Vancouver, British Columbia. As a registered nurse, I have worked as a research assistant for a university, in the OR (including transplant team), and in the NICU.

I suffered much physical and emotional trauma as a child. I had a childhood bicycle accident with a severe concussion, three serious car accidents, and other events that caused trauma to my head and spinal column. For decades, I have had many long-term symptoms of whiplash, including chronic pain and stiffness in the neck and shoulders, dizziness, numbness, weakness and tingling in my legs, and difficulty sleeping.

I attended a Tao Calligraphy Transformative Art healing event last week and was so excited when Master Sha created the Tao Bei Tao Calligraphy to heal and transform the back. When he led us in a Xi Qing Hu Zhuo breathing practice with the calligraphy, my neck grew very warm and I felt light-filled hands in the area. After the blessing, I felt space and lightness in my back and neck.

One week later, I am still shocked by my experience of the Tao Bei field healing. I have full sensation and range of motion in my back, shoulders, and neck. After suffering since childhood from back injuries, the peaceful energy in my back and throughout my body feels like a powerful, loyal friend who "has my back" in a loving way. I feel wonderful.

I am so deeply grateful to Master Sha and the Tao Bei Tao Calligraphy Transformative Art healing field for this remarkable healing.

— Marie Hope

Debilitating back pain resolved

I have worked as an office worker, typesetter, emergency room registrant, and administrative assistant for a family-owned company. I was widowed a few years ago and have a daughter and two sons, now grown.

I have been a spiritual seeker my entire life, a voracious reader and student of many modalities, including Quantum Touch, Melchizedek Method, Quick Pulse Training, and three levels of Reiki training and certification. I met Master Sha in 2006 at the Wesak Festival in Mt. Shasta, California. I am now a spiritual healer living in Illinois, USA.

I had severe lower back pain for a few days before joining a webcast with Master Sha. As he created the Tao Bei *Tao Calligraphy and proceeded to connect everyone with it, the pain in my back was completely resolved within a few minutes.*

Now, nearly two weeks later, the debilitating pain in my lower back has never returned. I am so very grateful!

— Teresa Anton

Quantum healing for back pain

I was raised in a beautiful Southern California town called Fallbrook. At the age of nineteen, my family and I moved to the Island of Hawaii. I am a single mother of five children and a grandmother to two of the most darling grandchildren. While living in Mountain View on the Island of Hawaii, I worked for many years as a certified nurse assistant specializing in Alzheimer's dementia care.

In 2017 I started to travel between Hawaii and Arizona for new employment opportunities. My work travels landed me in the behavioral health field serving those who struggle with severe drug and alcohol addiction. I knew I wanted to help more people, so I went back to school and recently graduated from the South-west Institute of Healing Arts in Tempe, Arizona with an Integrated Healing Arts Practitioner diploma. I have certifications as a professional life coach and Certified Intuitive Guide, and I hold a Bachelor of Divinity to serve as a spiritual life coach and interfaith minister. My passion in life is to serve those who are struggling with addictions and those who feel like they have lost hope. I want to serve through my professional/spiritual life coaching to help open hearts so they can feel love once again.

I have had challenges with my back off and on for years. For the past few weeks, I had been experiencing severe back pain, an 8 on a scale of 1 to 10. I was having difficulty sitting and standing due to painful cramping in my upper back.

I participated in a Tao Calligraphy healing session with Master Sha on January 11, 2022. During the healing with the Tao Bei Tao Calligraphy, I felt many blockages leave my back. Throughout the entire session, I felt a cool breeze moving through my back, some tingling, and, at times, a bit of heat. Now, more than twenty-four hours later, I still feel great. The pain has completely vanished and I can still feel energy moving in my back. It feels amazing!

— Dove Johnson

I can do and accomplish more

My career was in the pulp and paper industry as an instrumentation technician/electrician. I am married, have siblings, and live in Oregon, USA.

I have had three significant injuries in the past twenty to thirty years: concrete falling on my head, a bad fall on ice, and another fall that impacted my knees, hips, shoulder, and more. These accidents affected my ability to stand, walk, and climb ladders without pain. Even simple household chores have been a challenge.

We live on some acreage with considerable work to do outside. I was used to working in the yard, pasture, and garden, but I was having difficulty even walking outside without pain and had to sit down to relieve the pressure on my back.

I could no longer do my job of several decades, which required a lot of heavy lifting, climbing ladders and stairs, and awkward ergonomics at times, so I retired from my job early and am limited in what I am able to do. I have done physical work all my life, so not being able to move freely is very limiting. I have always enjoyed helping others, so being in pain and unable to help others has made my life incomplete.

I recently joined a Tao Calligraphy Transformative Art healing session with Master Sha during which he wrote a **Tao Bei** *(Tao Back) calligraphy and used it to offer a healing to all participants. With that healing, my lower back pain left! Immediately and ever since, I have been able to stand for longer periods and do and accomplish more. Before, I would need to stop and sit for a while to relieve my back pain when washing dishes or vacuuming.*

I had a chiropractor visit scheduled the next day. He has always adjusted my lower back or neck, but for the first time ever, he did not need to make these adjustments. My leg length had usually been off by one-half to three-quarters of an inch, but at this visit it was off by less than one-eighth of an inch. This is a huge improvement.

I am very grateful to Master Sha for his total, complete, and unconditional service to bring Tao Calligraphy Transformative Art to humanity.

— Patricia LeClair

Huge reduction in pain in two days

I live in Jerusalem and worked as an archaeologist. I left archaeology due to arthritis in my spinal column, hips, and knees. After that I worked with different healing modalities to help others and myself. I now have a soul healing business.

I have had mid-spinal column pain for at least six years. The pain would at times reach level 10 on a scale of 1–10. I would have to stop whatever I was doing and sit down with pillows to slowly release the pain. I tried different modalities to transform my back pain but nothing helped.

I recently joined a Tao Calligraphy Transformative Art healing session with Master Sha by webcast. After doing a self-healing breathing practice with the Tao Calligraphy Tao Bei, *my pain went down significantly. I awoke the next day feeling space in the area where there was once pain. The following day I again practiced with the Tao Bei calligraphy and received another big blessing: My pain went down ninety percent. This is a huge re-duction in just two days. It is beyond comprehension.*

I have felt comfort and space in the area for a few days now. Thank you, Master Sha. I am very grateful.

— Noura Barakat

Beyond powerful blessings

I live in Bareilly, a small town in Uttar Pradesh in India. I am a homemaker and artist who makes traditional Indian paintings. My family consists of my husband, mother-in-law, daughter, and a dog. I am a certified Tao Healing Hands Practitioner and feel blessed that I could serve family and friends with my Tao Hands during the pandemic.

I have had chronic back pain for seven years. I recently pulled a muscle in my upper back and was experiencing severe pain. On a scale of 1–10, it was 9. I was not able to move around well due to the pain. Painkillers had very little effect. I had to complete a painting order for my business as well as take care of my six-year-old daughter, but doing anything was nearly impossible due to the severity of the pain.

Last week, Master Sha offered healing blessings with the Tao Bei *Tao Calligraphy he had written. This was such a gift for me. I finished my day's work with a lot of difficulty and sat down for Master Sha's session with tears in my eyes due to the pain I was experiencing. After the session, I felt as though I had a brand-new back with no pain. I also feel more energetic and, even after working long hours, I don't feel any pain.*

Tao Calligraphy Transformative Art is beyond powerful.

Thank you, Master Sha. Greatest gratitude for this healing.

— Ritu Mehta

Great hope for total recovery

I live in Alphen aan den Rijn, a city with 75,000 inhabitants in the middle of the four major cities (Amsterdam, Rotterdam, the Hague, and Utrecht) in the western part of the Netherlands.

I competed with the Dutch national synchronized swimming team in international competitions, European Championships, and World Championships from 1974–1984. I received many medals in duet and group events and competed in the first Olympic Games for synchronized swimming in Los Angeles in 1984. I have a university degree in chemistry with a major in mathematics and worked for a multinational company in applied research and product development. I now work mostly on oral and written translations of educational and promotional materials into Dutch.

Ever since my last pregnancy over twenty years ago, I have experienced lower back pain that ranges from 2–8 with 10 being the most painful. I was no longer able to do any household activities and sports, which impacted my mood tremendously as sports had always been an important part of my life.

Once or twice a year, I would have severe stabbing back pain and my movements were heavily impaired. It could take weeks to recover. With the soul over matter techniques of Master Sha, these attacks have ceased for about eight years, but some pain remained with certain movements. Like many people with chronic pain, I got used to it and learned how to cope in my activities.

A few times a year, my lower back gradually becomes more stiff and painful and I see my shiatsu therapist for help. This week, my back was again so stiff and painful that I was going to make a shiatsu appointment. Then Master Sha wrote the Tao Calligraphy Tao Bei *and connected us with its field. My back pain immediately reduced by about fifty percent. The next morning, the pain was completely gone, and only with some extreme stretching could I feel a little stiffness. This is remarkable!*

I am so excited with this healing result and cannot wait for Master Sha's new book to be published so I have access to the Tao Calligraphy Tao Bei whenever I need. I have great hope for a total recovery. Deepest gratitude to the Tao Calligraphy Tao Bei Transformative Art Field.

— Catharina Eyken

Huge relief from Tao Bei blessing

I am a twenty-seven-year-old tai chi instructor in Toronto, Canada. I have passionately studied and practiced Zen-style meditation and tai chi daily for the past eight years.

I have been experiencing soreness and severe muscle tension in my lower back on and off for several months, which has affected my mobility and day-to-day activities. It is most painful when standing for a long period of time, walking a long distance, or even carrying groceries. I have tried many methods to get relief, but the results have only been temporary.

I received a Tao Calligraphy Transformative Art healing blessing for the back from Master Sha's Tao Bei *calligraphy during a recent online event. The moment Master Sha began writing the* Tao Bei *Tao Calligraphy, the pain in my back began to dissolve and I felt a pleasant warmth and tingling sensation in my lower back. The tension and constriction in my muscles began to release and I felt a decompressing sensation around my spinal column. This was a huge relief. Within several minutes, all of the pain in my back dissolved!*

It is now several days later and my back is still completely pain-free. I am amazed and so grateful for this huge healing. I am able to move around freely and without worrying about my back. In fact, my back is feeling so good that I have forgotten about it while going about my daily life.

Thank you, Master Sha. I am so grateful for Tao Calligraphy Transformative Art.

— Zakota Nesbitt

Extraordinary healing tool

I am originally from Berlin, Germany but have lived in Sweden for almost six years. I am a psychologist and yoga teacher. I have my own healing business and work as a spiritual teacher and healer where I combine all modalities I have learned, including psychology, yoga, Tao Science, and more, and offer personal consultations, classes, workshops, retreats, and programs for self-transformation. My focus is women's health and relation-ships. I also love to work with children and to support start-up companies.

I love to write, dance, paint, and be in nature. I enjoy hiking and spending time in the forest and collecting natural healing remedies from nature. I also love to eat and so I prepare a lot of healthy food. I love to study new wisdom and Master Sha's wisdom is always among my favorites.

I have suffered with back pain for many years, which has brought me on a path of deep self-healing. My chronic back pain is at level 7 on a scale of 1 to 10. At times it is difficult for me to get out of bed or to bend down, which makes many activities of daily living challenging: loading the dishwasher, doing laundry, gardening, lifting things, and shoveling snow. Pain impacts every aspect of my life. It is also difficult for me to practice or teach yoga as my movements are limited and some are quite painful.

In order to relieve my back pain, I have tried over the years all kinds of healing modalities and applied all I learned in psychol-ogy and yoga, as well as what I have learned about nutrition and balancing the body with natural remedies. Every morning, I sit with a heating pad for at least thirty minutes, apply healing oils, and practice self-healing in order to move around. The method that has always helped me the most is the soul over matter heal-ing techniques of Master Sha, especially the Tao Calligraphy Transformative Art. Applying Tao Calligraphy Transformative Art often brings me instant pain relief, even in situations where very strong painkillers don't help.

This morning I awoke with lower back pain at level 8. In the evening, I was able to join a Tao Calligraphy Transformative Art healing session with Master Sha. With the Tao Bei *Tao Calligraphy healing blessing and "inhaling positive and exhaling negative" breathing practice, I experienced profound relief from my chronic back pain after only twenty minutes. I experienced a lot of heat and energy movement in my lower back. At one point I felt very sharp pain in the lower back and, shortly after, in the upper back between my shoulder blades. It felt as though sharp blockages were removed. With that, a lot of the stiffness and tension in my entire back went away. I felt huge relief in my upper back muscles. The area relaxed and there is more softness now.*

I am deeply thankful for this very profound and rapid improvement. I will continue to do the practices recommended by Master Sha and I am looking forward to being completely pain-free with the help of the beautiful Tao Bei *Tao Calligraphy soon in Master Sha's next book. I have deep faith I will be healed with this extraordinary tool.*

— Magdalena Kusch

Art can heal!

I am an active and energetic seventy-year-old who rides a bicycle for transportation and relaxation. I live in New York City with my husband and partner of fifty years, whom I met when we were both Broadway performers. We share our home with our little dog, Shen. I have been self-employed with a private acupuncture practice since 1980 and was one of a small group of acupuncturists in New York who worked for many years to have acupuncture recognized and licensed as a profession. In the late 1990s I served as President of the National Acupuncture Organization (AAOM) and had the opportunity to meet with representatives from around the world to establish standards of practice. An interest in Chinese medicine, Buddhism, and Taoist philosophy have been a continuous thread in my life.

In 2004 I suffered a chiropractic accident. I had an undiagnosed bulging disc in my spine and was given a strong manual adjustment, from which I saw stars! About three hours later, I literally could not sit, stand, or walk. My body just collapsed in a lump when I attempted to move. It appeared that the adjustment broke off a piece of the disc, which lodged itself between two vertebrae. I saw a surgeon who advised me to wait and do nothing, believing that my body would eventually remove the material and heal itself. I spent two months lying flat on my back and an additional three months in extreme pain. Since that time, I have had consistent discomfort at a pain level of 2–3 out of 10 on good days, but with many more days in the 5–7 range. Acupuncture and qigong have helped me manage my back pain, but never with any lasting effect. In addition, scoliosis started becoming evident in my spine about three years ago.

I was particularly uncomfortable on the day of a Tao Calligraphy Transformative Art healing session with Master Sha last week. During the Tao Bei Tao Calligraphy self-healing breathing practice and blessing, I felt a light coolness in my back but there was no immediate change in the discomfort I was experiencing. About five hours later, the pain and discomfort were totally gone. It is quite amazing that art can heal!

The next evening, my back began to have a slight whisper of discomfort. I laid down, connected with the Tao Bei *Tao Calligraphy, and chanted. I experienced a cool sensation within my spine. The spine seemed to elongate, adjust, and relax. My back has been pretty much pain-free since the healing session. There have been a few moments of slight discomfort, but as soon as I notice it, I pause, connect with the* Tao Bei *calligraphy in my mind, and the discomfort disappears.*

I am incredibly grateful for this healing and for Tao Calligraphy Transformative Art.

— Robbee Fian, L.Ac.

All symptoms in my neck, back, and hip are gone

I have two children, a twenty-nine-year-old son and twenty-six-year-old daughter. My parents live independently. I have one brother and one sister. I have worked as an occupational therapist for nearly ten years at an adult physical rehabilitation center. I love to walk in nature and my favorite interest is Tao Calligraphy writing. I was drawn to the power of Tao Calligraphy because I realized in my work that we cannot completely heal and treat all sicknesses, especially neurological diseases for which there is no conventional treatment.

Eighteen years ago, I fell at work and ever since sometimes feel tension or stiffness in my neck. A few weeks ago, I had fluctuating back pain. Two weeks ago, I tested positive for Covid. Along with Covid, my muscles and lower back hurt, and my right hip also hurt, which was new for me.

After doing breathing practice and receiving remote healing blessings from Master Sha with the Tao Bei *Tao Calligraphy, all of the symptoms disappeared. Following the first healing session, my neck felt very flexible and relaxed. After the second healing session, my hip pain was also gone. With the third healing session, I felt a shift in the vertebrae at the base of my neck. My spine literally felt as though it moved back into its proper place. Several days have gone by, and my lower back no longer hurts, even when bending forward.*

I connected with the Tao Bei *Tao Calligraphy several times a day and chanted in order to support my healing. My practice was minimal compared to the healing I have received: all symptoms in my neck, back, and hip are gone. This is astounding!*

I am very grateful to the Tao Calligraphy Transformative Art Field and Master Sha for this extraordinary healing.

— Gerd Geukens

৪ ৪ ৫

Because Tao Calligraphy Transformative Art carries a Tao Source Field with Source love and light and Source frequency and vibration, healing with the *Tao Bei* Tao Calligraphy is not limited to the back. For example, the person in the last story above shared about her relief from neck and hip pain. The Source Field is a quantum field. Here is one story of deep transformation for issues not directly related to the back from the Tao Calligraphy *Tao Bei* Field.

Breathing deeply again after being in the Tao Calligraphy Transformative Art Field

I am single with no children, thirty-three years old, and live in Germany. My family left Russia to live in Germany nineteen years ago. Both my parents have transitioned. I work as a laboratory assistant and have always been interested in alternative and spiritual healing methods. I enjoy doing spiritual practice and am on my own healer journey as a Tao Healing Hands Practitioner.

Nearly four weeks ago, I tested positive for COVID-19 and went through a challenging time with breathing difficulties, coughing, overall weakness, and more. I experienced pressure in my lungs, which made breathing at full capacity very difficult. I was also coughing a lot and had to use an inhaler at night to open my bronchia. Because of my diagnosis, I had to quarantine. A friend and my sister supported me by bringing me groceries and more. The first week of the COVID-19 infection was very difficult to go through.

I returned to work a few days ago, but still had difficulty breathing freely and felt as though I was not getting enough oxygen. I was still coughing, my body felt weak, and I was exhausted after work. I still felt congestion in my lungs and had trouble breathing at full capacity after a few hours of wearing a mask.

Right after I returned to work, Master Sha offered two huge Tao Calligraphy Transformative Art practice sessions with the Tao Bei (Tao Back) calligraphy. My back itself was not an issue for me. Yet, I could feel the pure energy and light entering my body and opening spaces inside. It felt as though a light breeze came to my lungs and I immediately started to receive more oxygen and breathe more deeply. The pressure in my lungs decreased. Then I experienced a huge release of old emotions related with the loss of my parents. (In traditional Chinese medicine, grief is related to the lungs.)

The day after being in the Tao Calligraphy Tao Bei Transformative Art Field, I felt much more energized and could breathe at normal capacity. Now, several days have passed, and I have not had to use the medicinal inhaler once. I have more energy and stamina. I have no shortness of breath, even when wearing a mask. Being outside and breathing the cold winter air no longer gives me any tightness in my lungs.

I believe it would have been very difficult for me to recover as quickly and as completely without access to this high-frequency field. I am deeply grateful for the Tao Calligraphy Transformative Art Field at this time when so many people need healing.

— Anastaja Schmidt

ॐ ॐ ॐ

I thank each of you who shared your story, including the many more of you whose stories are not included in this book. I am delighted that you have received great benefits from the Tao Calligraphy Transformative Art Field. I thank you for your gratitude and appreciation.

I also offer my greatest gratitude to Tao Source, to the Tao Calligraphy Transformative Art Field, and to all who have empowered me to be your servant. I am honored to serve you. I am honored to serve humanity with Tao Calligraphy Transformative Art.

I love my heart and soul
I love all humanity
Join hearts and souls together
Love, peace, and harmony
Love, peace, and harmony

Scientific Research on Tao Calligraphy Field Transformation by Peter Hudoba, M.D.

AFTER INITIAL SUCCESS in a research project on cancer patients in 2001, a group of physicians and psychologists established Sha Research Foundation in San Francisco, California to document the effectiveness of soul over matter healing or, simply, soul healing.

Over the past eighteen years, a number of clinicians and researchers have been involved in various research studies. From the very beginning, Sha Research Foundation has applied the same rigorous standards used in clinical research studies conducted by universities, utilizing conventional research study designs and standardized, well-recognized research questionnaires to assess results.

Sha Research Foundation's research teams have completed nineteen clinical studies in which a total of approximately six hundred fifty subjects participated. Research results consistently showed improvement in various aspects of wellbeing. In some cases, the subject's illness was markedly improved or even completely resolved. Thirty-one research papers based on these studies have been presented at medical conferences worldwide.

Following are summaries of some of our recent research studies related to Tao Calligraphy Transformative Art.

Chronic Pain

In 2019–2020, a clinical research study led by Dr. Consuelo Fernandez was conducted on chronic pain at a pain clinic in the United States. The study initially involved fifty-one patients, of whom forty-five completed the study. Patients used meditation with Tao Calligraphy Transformative Art and daily mantra chanting for an average of eight minutes a day. Some subjects chanted as much as thirty minutes daily.

To measure changes in subjects' pain levels, the research team used the McGill Pain Questionnaire (SF–MPQ), a well-verified research tool used for more than four decades around the world and recognized as a valid, reliable, and sensitive multidimensional measure to evaluate pain.

This study documented statistically significant improvement in the intensity of the subjects' pain. It is quite interesting to me that even with the subjects' limited meditation time with the Tao Calligraphy Field, there was still a statistically significant improvement in their pain.

The results of the study were presented at the 2020 AIHM (Academy of Integrative Health & Medicine) People Planet

Purpose Annual Conference in San Diego, California and at the 2021 SIO (Society for Integrative Oncology) International Conference in Baltimore, Maryland.

Unipolar Depression

In 2020–2021 Dr. Katharina Balonwu led a clinical research study at a psychology clinic in Germany. The study involved twenty-three patients who used meditation with the Tao Calligraphy Field and mantra chanting.

To measure the changes in unipolar depression (major depression), the research team used BDI I, BDI II, PHQ–9, HAM–D, and HAM–A questionnaires. These are standard questionnaires used by clinicians and researchers to assess depression for both clinical and research purposes. All questionnaires documented statistically significant improvement in depression, as much as sixty-seven percent.

The study was conducted at the height of the global coronavirus pandemic. It is well-known that circumstances related to the pandemic (economic hardship, social isolation, challenges in household relationships, anxiety, fear, loss of loved ones, etc.) triggered or exacerbated existing mental illness for many people worldwide. One would therefore expect that patients in the study would be much worse also. On the contrary, those patients who meditated in the Tao Calligraphy Field improved as much as sixty-seven percent. For me, this is the most striking aspect of this study.

The results of the study were presented at the annual conference of the European Congress for Integrative Medicine in London, United Kingdom in 2021.

Breast Cancer

In 2020–2021 a clinical study led by Dr. Magdalena Bright involved patients in the United States with breast cancer. The study initially involved fifty-nine patients, of whom eighteen completed the study. The subjects used meditation in the Tao Calligraphy Field and mantra chanting, both on their own and jointly in a group with other study subjects.

To measure the improvement in the wellbeing of the subjects, the research team used the well-known EORTC Standardized Quality of Life Questionnaire QLQ–C30, which is well-verified and recognized as a reliable and valid research tool used around the world for many years to assess the quality of life of cancer patients.

Over the course of the six-month-long study, subjects experienced statistically significant improvement in their wellbeing, which is very encouraging. The results were presented in 2021 at the Society for Integrative Oncology 16th International Conference: Advancing the Science and Art of Integrative Oncology in Baltimore, Maryland.

We present next a summary of the second paper that Dr. Magdalena Bright and her team, Joan Luk, L.Ac. and Michell Rudacille, presented. This presentation was heart-touching to me in that it documents how using the Tao

Calligraphy Field in clinical settings positively influences not only patients, but healthcare providers as well. May it serve as a great inspiration to all of us.

Background: The authors describe their personal experience while conducting research and leading group mindfulness practice sessions with breast cancer patients.

Main Concept: Caring for breast cancer patients has challenges and demands that often lead to burnout and frustration in both healthcare providers and patients. Professional guidelines that involve boundaries and standard approaches and clinical research with its zeal for standard research methodologies have reduced essential aspects of human interaction. Caring for patients suffering from cancer causes physical, psychological, and emotional stress in healthcare providers. These factors can leave cancer patients feeling lonely, isolated, and fearful. Can mindfulness practice with the Tao Calligraphy Field improve human interaction and connection and increase provider and patient satisfaction with breast cancer care? Three women conducted a study incorporating integrative medicine in the form of mindfulness practices with patients receiving conventional breast cancer treatment.

Description: The cancer research project was done as a key component of a PhD thesis. Two volunteer facilitators and one researcher conducted mindfulness group practice sessions with eighteen breast cancer patients using the Tao Calligraphy Field and mantra chanting five times a week for six months.

The researcher and facilitators felt inspired and found purpose in what they did to guide and support other women in difficult situations. The human connection, support, love, and care created a close comradery within the team that was truly cherished and heart-touching. The women who were subjects in the study felt that they could share their thoughts, fears, struggles, and successes openly with the group and found this immensely helpful in their journey with breast cancer.

Significance: Including mindfulness practices with Tao Calligraphy provided a positive environment for human connection that essentially led to a healing process for both researchers and patients. Researchers felt connected and deeply fulfilled and research subjects felt loved and cared for.

ಬಿ ಐ ಲ

Finally, we present a heart-touching testimony from a research subject with chronic low back pain in his own words, edited slightly so as not to identify the subject:

I am an (age removed) year-old man. I had an accident in 2005 that resulted in a broken back in the lumbar section (L2), which led to a laminectomy with L1, L2, and L3 fusion of the lumbar spine secured by a pair of titanium rods in my back. The accident traumatized me and I received medical treatments for the following diagnoses: chronic pain, depression, and anxiety.

Prior to the accident, my career path was well under way. How-ever, my career was abruptly interrupted fifteen years ago by the accident, which ended my vocation and nearly ended my life. My return to the same status and career path was lost to fate and deferred to others. Nothing was ever the same after that traumatic event.

Although the traditional medical model of treatment that I re-ceived throughout the decade-and-a-half was amazingly helpful, and I truly am appreciative for being put back together, the road to recovery was arduous and fraught with enduring challenges of pain and suffering. They helped with my struggles with back pain, depression, and anxiety. I had been making progress in my recovery by the many means received through traditional medi-cine and alternatives, but I continued to suffer from pain, de-pression, and anxiety. I continued to seek a solution for my painful conditions and was introduced to Dr. and Master Sha and his group of healers. Last year, I enrolled in the research study.

Since my enrollment into the Tao Calligraphy tracing healing research program last year, I have practiced the Tao Calligraphy healing method on a daily basis, along with weekly progress check-in and regular monitoring with (identifiers removed as this study is ongoing)*, who has also monitored my progress periodically with measuring tools. Since joining the Tao Callig-raphy research study, my symptoms have improved tremen-dously in just a short period of one year. Not only is my back pain reduced, depression lifting, and anxiety improved, but other nerve damage-related conditions as well. For example, prior to the accident fifteen years ago, I had daily bowel move-ments, but since the spinal nerve damage, my bowel movements* became very irregular, slow, sluggish, and weekly rather than daily. The unexpected additional benefit of the Tao Calligraphy tracing program is that my bowel movements have increased to two to three times a week and, recently, three to five times weekly. My energy level has increased and is much more than when compared to a year ago.

Like I said, my back pain, depression, and anxiety are so much improved that I can hardly believe it. It is truly a miracle. My physical and emotional recovery progress was significant and I have so much to be grateful for: my family, friends, colleagues, medical and alternative approaches, self-help spiritual dynamics, etc. But I was still in pain and suffering, and my senior title job status was reduced several months before I enrolled into the research study. I had to do something. What led me to seek out Tao Calligraphy as part of my treatment was a lecture given by Dr. and Master Sha and his blessings that I remembered from before. A feeling of hope that a very good possibility for true healing existed was restored.

Since my enrollment and daily practice in the Tao Calligraphy program with weekly follow-up sessions, I have been progressively improving over the course of the past year. My schoolwork has improved and I have fewer sick days on the job than I have had for the past fifteen years. Prior to the Tao Calligraphy program, I was calling out sick too often according to my employer. That is not an issue anymore and I feel much better. I do not feel ashamed of myself anymore. I have an acceptance and a sense of hope like never before because of Dr. and Master Sha's Tao Calligraphy program. Thank you.

It is a joy and privilege to conduct research using Master Sha's Tao Calligraphy Transformative Art Field and Soul Power. Over the years, we have had many gifted and wonderful professionals and supportive teams join Sha Research Foundation to collaborate on our studies. Nothing would have been achieved if not for the hundreds of research subjects who gave their heart and dedication to support our work. We are immensely grateful to all of them. Above all, we cannot be grateful enough to Master Sha, who has made all of these "miracles" possible.

If you would like to review the presentations in more depth or learn more about Sha Research Foundation, please visit www.ShaResearchFoundation.com.

Conclusion

I HAVE A DREAM that humanity will pay more and more attention to self-healing. I honor all medical professionals and all alternative and complementary medicines, as well as all ways to improve our health and happiness.

The message I always share with humanity is:

I have the power to heal myself.
You have the power to heal yourself.
Together we have the power to heal the world.

I have studied Chinese energy and spiritual healing, including tai chi, qi gong, gong fu, *I Ching*, and feng shui, as well as Western medicine and traditional Chinese medicine. I have created Tao Calligraphy.

Through my whole life's study, I have realized in my heart and soul a one-sentence secret for healing and transforming all life:

All challenges in health, relationships, finances, and the spiritual journey are due to negative information, energy, and matter; Tao Calligraphy carries Source most-positive information, energy, and matter, with Source love, light, and frequency, which could transform negative information, energy, and matter in every aspect of life.

This book and subsequent books in the Tao Calligraphy series are bringing the Tao Calligraphy Transformative Art Source Field to humanity to transform every aspect of life.

Recall the ancient secret wisdom: da Dao zhi jian, *the greatest Tao is extremely simple*. The Tao Calligraphy Transformative Art Field is the da Dao zhi jian way to serve humanity in every aspect of life.

It is one of my biggest dreams to serve all humanity. I have created thousands of heart-touching and moving healing results. I do not promise anything. I support all medical and healing systems worldwide. I am a servant for humanity. I am delighted to create the Tao Calligraphy book series to serve.

The Tao Calligraphy Field brings Source power to humanity in order to serve you in every aspect of your life. This is the first book in the Tao Calligraphy series.

Practice. Practice. Practice.
Heal. Heal. Heal.
Transform. Transform. Transform.

I love my heart and soul
I love all humanity
Join hearts and souls together
Love, peace, and harmony
Love, peace, and harmony

Upcoming Books in the Tao Calligraphy Series

UPCOMING VOLUMES WILL focus on:

- Healing the Immune System

- Healing Depression and Anxiety

- Healing Knee Pain

- Healing Fear

- Healing Shoulder Pain

- Healing Anger

- Healing Heart Issues

- Healing Grief

- Healing the Kidneys

- Healing Worry

In each book of the Tao Calligraphy series, I will write a new and different Tao Calligraphy. I will repeat the key fundamental wisdom and knowledge. I will lead readers to practice in the Tao Calligraphy Field created by one or more Tao Calligraphies in each book.

Manufactured by Amazon.ca
Bolton, ON

24809407R00111